A BETTER READING WORKSHOP

Reading Speed for Comprehension

BOOK 1

Robert R. Potter

Globe Book Company, Inc.
New York / Chicago / Cleveland

ROBERT R. POTTER received his B.S. from the Columbia University School of General Studies and his M.A. and Ed.D. from Teachers College, Columbia University.

Dr. Potter has been a teacher of English in the New York City School System, a research associate for Project English at Hunter College, and a teacher of English at the Litchfield (Conn.) High School. He has held professorships at the State University of New York and at the University of Connecticut.

Dr. Potter is the author of Globe's *Beyond Time and Space, Stories of Surprise and Wonder, Tales of Mystery and the Unknown, Myths and Folktales Around the World, The Reading Road to Writing Series, Writing a Research Paper, Writing Sense,* and *Language Workshop.*

Better Reading Workshop is based in part on the work of Joseph C. Gainsburg, Ph.D., and Samuel I. Spector, Ph.D., as contained in their book *Better Reading.* The author and the publisher acknowledge their valuable contribution to this text.

Editor: Nancy R. Hitchner
Photo Editor: Adelaide Garvin Ungerland
Illustrations: Mel Erikson
Opening Illustrations: Heidi Steinberger
Text and Cover Design: Caliber Design Planning, Inc.
Typesetting: York Graphic Services, Inc.
Photo Credits: Polish Embassy—42
New York Times/Fred R. Conrad—23
H. Armstrong Roberts—32
United Press International—2, 14, 15
U.S. Fish and Wildlife Service/Rex Gary Schmidt—21
Wide World Photos—13

ISBN: 0-87065-446-2
Copyright © 1984, 1978 by Globe Book Company, Inc.
50 West 23rd Street, New York, N.Y. 10010

Published simultaneously in Canada by Globe/Modern Curriculum Press.

PRINTED IN THE UNITED STATES OF AMERICA

9 8 7 6 5 4 3 2 1

CONTENTS

▷1 Skimming to Find Information Quickly

▷2 Reading by Word Groups

3 ▶ Applying Your Skimming Skills

4 ▶ Testing Your Reading Skills

Getting Started

So you think you need help in reading? Welcome to the club! Very few people, of any age, read as well as they could—or should. BETTER READING is what this workbook is all about.

First, what does the word *reading* really mean? That question isn't as simple as it sounds. Think about it for a minute or two. Then take a pencil and underline the words in **heavy black type** that you think describe a part of "reading."

Reading is . . .
- **recognizing letter shapes.**
- **knowing word parts.**
- **sounding out words.**
- **knowing words.**
- **seeing how words go together.**
- **understanding punctuation symbols.**
- **finding main ideas.**
- **thinking.**
- **"reading between the lines."**
- **skimming.**
- **rereading.**
- **remembering.**
- **predicting outcomes.**
- **understanding charts and graphs.**
- **knowing where to find information.**

By now you should realize a very important fact: Reading is made up of *all* these skills—and many more. It's easy to see why people who lack these skills have a hard time reading. Good readers have learned these skills. And just as important, they know exactly which skills to use for each particular reading task.

For each purpose you may have, there is a proper kind of reading. There is a special kind of reading skill to use. Knowing which skills to use for which purposes will make your reading much more interesting. No longer will reading send you off into dreamland. No longer will you risk getting *F*s on tests that call for reading.

Again, welcome to the club! Give the job some patience and effort. Soon you will read with an ease and a power you have never known before.

 SKIMMING TO FIND INFORMATION QUICKLY

Skim-m-ing for Speed

▶ People read for many different purposes. In school, your purpose is often to learn and remember all that you read. But is this *always* your purpose in reading? Of course it isn't.

Suppose you were driving a car and saw the scene pictured below through your windshield. You might be confused, but would you bother to read everything? For instance, would you read the words on the backs of the three trucks? No. If your purpose was simply to get where you wanted to go, you would read only the signs that might help you reach that goal.

Many times you are interested in only *part* of what you read. You speed up. This kind of reading is called SKIMMING. First, you must have your reading goal firmly in mind. Then you let your eyes wander over the words. Finally, you find what you are looking for.

When you do find it, you ought to read with care. But until you find it, you should do the following:

1. Read rapidly.
2. Keep going, and do not look back.
3. Slide over unimportant words.
4. Don't try to remember everything; just go after what you want.
5. Be sure you understand the purpose of the skimming.
6. *Stop and read with great care* the moment you find the information you're looking for. ▪

SKILL BUILDER 1

Directions: Below is a selection called "Sign Language." Following it is a list of words. Your purpose is to find these words in the selection. Don't try to learn all the facts. Just skim, or glance ahead, until you find each word you are looking for. When you find it, write the number of the line in which it appears in the blank provided. The first one has been done for you.

SIGN LANGUAGE

1   Do you want a good hobby? Start studying signs. Write down signs that interest you. If you
2 can, take pictures of them.
3   Some signs are very clever. A sign for a bank in Oklahoma reads, "Every spring we get
4 loanly." In Ohio, a garbage service says, "Our business is picking up." In New York, a frozen
5 custard stand is called CUSTARD'S LAST STAND.
6   Some churches have interesting signs: OPEN SUNDAYS! "Come in and have your faith
7 lifted." "Thou shalt not park here. All sinners towed away."
8   Other signs have unusual spellings. A New Mexico garage says C US FOR SERVICE. A
9 small building at a New England camp has a sign, TO LET. The "I" in the middle is missing.
10   Still other signs are confusing. Look at the picture on page 2. It shows a street in Detroit,
11 Michigan. The signs confuse drivers who see them for the first time. Drivers who know the area
12 are not confused. The two top signs refer to Cabot, the street before the signs (not shown). The
13 other signs are for drivers who go on to Addison Road.

WORD	LINE	WORD	LINE
1. SUNDAYS	6	11. Cabot	
2. SERVICE		12. New England	
3. CUSTARD'S		13. sinners	
4. TO LET		14. garage	
5. Oklahoma		15. bank	
6. Detroit		16. hobby	
7. Ohio		17. picture	
8. Addison		18. pictures	
9. New York		19. spring	
10. New Mexico		20. refer	

Find That Job!

RN or LPN wanted for night shift. Knight Nursing Home, Cambridge, a 20-mile drive. Apply in person only between 9 and 4.

Mother's helper for Jul. & Aug. About 5 hrs. daily. Most day work but must be available Sat. nights. Manfred Hill section, 5 min. to bus. Mrs. Luzzatto, 426-3536.

Clerk wanted at KIDDIE WORLD. Must know clothing and like children. Apply in person, 420 N. Main.

SECRETARY-BOOKKEEPER WANTED. Top firm offers top money to top person. Write Box 1224, World-Herald.

Over 500 jobs in labor-market area for economically disadvantaged youth. Legal wage for 25-hour week. Ages 14–21. Apply Employment Service, Government Bldg., 18 Maxwell St.

Dishwasher, part-time, for summer only. Good opty for student. Must be free 4 nights a week and on call. Apply in person, Tripps Steak House, 101 Dean Bancroft Hwy.

FUN JOB! Make donuts in downtown window. Apply in person at The Sweet Tooth, corner Main and 12th.

District Manager for pharmacy chain. Salary to 25M. Coffee-and-cake persons need not apply. Box 1226, World-Herald.

Lawn mower wanted for full-time park work. Must know machinery. See Mr. Fox, Room 202, City Hall.

RNs for growing well-child clinic. Top state pay scale and full benefits after 3 mos. Work 8:30–4:00 downtown. 426-5121.

Factory workers. Minimum wage while we train you for permanent position. Allentown. Call 939-7275

Secretary wanted for public health nursing office. Some experience necessary. Central location. 222-5759.

TRAINED MECHANIC FOR FOREIGN CARS. Must know diesel, fuel injection. Top $. Send training and experience to International Rally Center, 306 S. Main.

Couple for house and estate work. References required. Box 1136, World-Herald.

Mature person to assist elderly man. Must drive, play chess. Salary depends on hours and ability. This is not a short-term job. Reynold's Lake area. Box 1197, World-Herald.

BIG MONEY STUFFING ENVELOPES. $250 per 1000 possible. Work home. For details write Wm. Moore, 1035 Griswold S.E., Grand Rapids, Mich. 49507.

Supermarket check-out clerk at west side Top Value. Experience required. We are an Equal Opportunity Employer.

Career selling job. Prior experience not necessary. We train you for long-term income. See Mr. Cutter, Rm. 16, Route 6 Motel, all day Sat. and Sun. p.m.

Waitress wanted at McInnis Diner, Rt. 206 past airport.

TIRED of the 9 to 5 routine? Be your own boss by calling us at 939-7317.

Great chance till Labor Day! Butler National Bank needs college student to take place of workers on vacation. Some opportunity as teller. Person chosen must be intelligent, careful, neat, polite. For interview call Mr. Samuels at 939-0166.

TYPIST, PART-TIME. Must put up with bad handwriting and ill-tempered writer. 199-6362.

Hairdressers needed. License a must. Creative work. Glamorous clients. Call Mrs. Ariel at 655-8245.

Are you a trained dental assistant? We are a growing practice looking for a responsible person. Knowledge of X-ray a must. See Dr. Silver or Dr. Rajam, 98 Jefferson Blvd.

GAL/GUY FRIDAY. Up to $300 a week. Word-processing skills needed. Contact Great Books, State St.

HIRING NOW. Telephone salespeople. If you enjoy speaking on the phone this job is for you. Salary plus commission. Don't wait! 224-7323.

Manager needed for pet shop. Our animals require expert care. Call for interview with owner, 656-5779.

MECHANICAL ENGINEER. Experience in systems design plus degree required. Contact T. Ruiz, Con-Fab Systems, Route 30, Hooper Falls.

▶ Look at the opposite page. Where does it come from? It's from the help-wanted section of a newspaper, of course.

Few people read help-wanted ads for fun. If you were reading the ads shown, you would have a clear purpose in mind—to find a job. You'd probably look for ads that call for your particular skills, work experience, and available time. So you wouldn't want to read every word of every ad. Instead, *key words* would help you spot just the right ones. For instance, you might have worked as a baby-sitter in the past. Skimming the ads quickly, you come to the words *mother's helper*. These key words are your signal to read the ad carefully.

The first few words of most ads are enough to signal *yes, maybe,* or *no.* ▪

SKILL BUILDER 2

Directions: Complete each item that follows by skimming the ads on page 4. First, underline one or two key words in the item that will help you spot the right ad. Then skim, and write the information called for on the line. Be sure you understand the terms listed below before you begin.

benefits—health insurance, vacation pay, etc.
couple—husband and wife
LPN—licensed practical nurse

prior—completed, coming before
RN—registered nurse
M—$1,000

Suppose you . . .

1. . . . wanted to work as a mother's helper during the summer. Your employer's name might be

_____

2. . . . had always wanted to work in a children's shop. There is a job offered at a shop named

_____

3. . . . knew about lawn mowers and wanted a job mowing lawns full time. You could stop in to see

_____

4. . . . were a college student studying banking. A summer job in your field is available at

_____

5. . . . were a registered nurse. Your *best* bet would probably be to pick up the phone and dial

_____

6. . . . had married and the two of you wanted to work as a couple. You could write to

_____

7. . . . were a good secretary but knew nothing about bookkeeping. Your *best* bet would be to call

_____

8. . . . had once clerked in a supermarket and liked the job. You might be interested in working at

_____

9. How many ads contain box numbers instead of phone numbers?

_____

10. The law says that jobs should not be advertised for "men only" or "women only." Which ad seems to break this law?

_____

Using a Building Directory

302	ADORNO ROBERT	401	JOHNS SERVICE CENTERS
LBY	ARROW BUS LINE	LBY	KING EATS INC
1001	AT-HOME INSTRUCTION	601	LAMP WORLD
1004	MAIL ROOM	603	LUNDQUIST IRA
301	ATWOOD GROVER MD	203	MAPS UNLIMITED
405	AUTO FINANCERS	204	DELIVERIES
801	BATTAGLIA JOYCE	501	MODERN FLOORS INC
205	BERMAN & BERMAN	602	NAUTS G
602	BLATZ SHEMAN CPA	503	NODINE MEATS
402	CAREER APPAREL INC	802	NORBERT ASSOCIATES
LBY	CASH NOW	804	NU-LIFE
701	CASH ROGER	202	OPPENHEIMER AIDA
305	COLMAN IRA	901	PRINTS INC
605	DWYER JOHN ATTY	905	RUSSELL VICTOR
7 FL	EXCITING SALES CORP	303	SAM BONORO INC
703	DELIVERIES	1005	TAXI SERVICE INC
705	MAIL ROOM	LBY	DRIVERS ROOM
203	FABRIC SHOPS	304	WATKINS BROTHERS INC
902	FISHBEIN SOL DDS	201	YOHE
502	INLAID GRAPHICS	601	ZABF

Have you ever been in a large office building? If so, you probably saw a building directory in the lobby. That directory listed the people and companies with offices in the building. It was organized in alphabetical order.

Building directories can be confusing. Commas and periods are often left out. The people who work for a company are usually not listed as individuals. But sometimes they are listed. Also, people are usually listed by last name. But sometimes the listing starts with the first name. This happens when a person's name is also the name of a company.

Look at the young man in the picture. What might his purpose be in reading? Suppose that he wants to find a company he's heard of that makes loans for new cars. If so, he should be *skimming* the directory to find just what he wants. He should also remember to look for key words like *auto* or *finance* if he can't find *car* or *loan*. ∎

SKILL BUILDER 3

Directions: Look at the building directory on page 6. Notice that the names are listed in alphabetical order, from <u>Adorno</u> through <u>Zabrieski</u>. Then complete the following items as fast as you can. Be sure that you understand the abbreviations listed below before you begin.

Atty.—attorney, lawyer
Fl.—floor
Lby.—lobby

C.P.A.—Certified Public Accountant, an expert bookkeeper
D.D.S.—Doctor of Dental Surgery, a highly trained dentist
M.D.—Doctor of Medicine, a doctor

Suppose you . . .

1. . . . were taking a package to Joyce Battaglia. You would go to room number

_____

2. . . . had a package to deliver to Maps Unlimited. You would go to room number

_____

3. . . . had heard there was a good dentist in the building. Now you've forgotten his name. It is

_____

4. . . . had a job interview with Sam Bonoro. You would go to room number

_____

5. . . . were a private detective. You want to talk to a certain taxi driver. Your best bet would be to hang around

_____

6. . . . had just seen a bad accident on the street outside. A doctor who might be in the building is named

_____

7. . . . needed a loan for a new car. You would go to the office of

_____

8. . . . had a message for Roger Cash. The directory tells that he probably works for

_____

9. . . . were told to see Joe Watkins. You might find him in room number

_____

10. . . . were selling office machines. The largest company in this building seems to be

_____

Winning Numbers

A-Aim

672-5888 A-1 Pizza Palace 25NMain
672-0080 A-PRIME STEAK HOUSE 136Center
        AA see Alcoholics Anonymous
672-3572 AA BRUNELL CO INC 3Main
489-5176 AAA MOTOR CLUB 131Maple
417-0175 ABC Hair Stylists 10Church
672-0146 AC ELECTRIC 4W17
672-0196 –Customer Service
MILL RV AOK AIRPORT SERVICE 36TownLineRd
364-8008   Mill River
489-0021 Abalone, Arthur V 3MillersLa
324-0125 Abata I J AbataLa
417-5202 Abbott William 36Sanders
417-5437 Abbott William E 43Church
489-0188 Abramowitz Jack 4DarkRiverRd
417-5442 Abrams N W 46Elm
324-5388 Accardo Richard E dntst
        LongMeadowLa
672-5287 ACE TRAVEL SERVICE 17Main
489-5866 Acerbo Lucy Mrs 14Maple
417-5616 Acheson Samuel 36Church
417-5874 Acker Eric L 570Jordon
489-5741 Ackerman Albert 37HoustonRd
672-0087 Ackerman Milton 101Center
489-5458 Ackerman W S 37Elm
489-0272 Ackermann Orlando 23MapleTerr
417-5985 Ackerson Nancy 43State
672-5997 Ackley&Sanders 4NMain
672-5786 Ackman Michael 47Center
324-5681 Ackner Lea T 17RogersPl
672-0057 Ackroyd Manuel 21W4
489-5262 ACME ARTESIAN WELLS
        47DarkRiverRd
672-0012 Acme Beef Co 7E12
324-5627 Acopolos Hector 77Maxwell
672-5879 Acorn Book Shop 8Main
417-5729 Acosta Juan 403Jordan
672-0016 Acropolis Builders 131Center
672-5243 ACT II RESTRNT 7Main
672-0284 Acuna Carlos 23E7
672-0059 Adair Alvin 37W12
417-5375 Adam Eve Mrs 14Church
324-0334 Adamec H H 44Wyoming
324-5954 Adams Alice 14Maxwell
672-0144 Adams Heating Co 22NMain
417-5486 Adams Vicky 14Sanders
324-5042 Adano Peppino 71ParkAv
417-5861 Adkins Thomas 9Church
672-5240 Adkins Wyler 141Center
672-5309 Adorno Bernard MD 7Main
417-5652   Res 300Jordan
489-5835 Adorno Eduardo 48Eagle
672-0030 Adrian C 14E12
672-5344 Adroit Cleaners 14NMain
417-5305 Adsit Ronald 10Church
417-0086 Adult-Youth League 12Church
324-0127 Advance Printers 4Lister
417-5104 Advent Methodist Church 4Adams
489-5167 ADVENTURE SPORTS SHOP
        36DarkRiverRd

672-0298 Advertising Sales Co 2W13
417-5539 Adwin Ellen Miss 22Elm
489-0005 Aeder Rollins 24Eagle
672-5756 Aerenson Robert R 11W11
672-5725 Aero Carters Inc 40E7
324-0231 Affe Gerald 77Summer
672-0319 Affen Margot 22E8
672-5115 Affiliated Grocers 40W14
417-5348 Affron L P 80Sanders
672-5047 AFIE 17Center
672-5523 Afro-American Photos 14E3
672-5674 After Dark Boutique 7Main
672-5873 After Hours Club 3Main
489-0279 Afton Harry 22HoustonRd
324-5921 Agard Walter 89HarvestDr
417-0390 Agata Sandra 21State
324-5260 Agate Harold 14ParkAv
324-5187 Agate Linda 14ParkAv
489-0330 Agatielli Pat 13Maple
672-5258 Agee Alex 17E11
672-0189 AGENCIA HISPANA 17NMain
672-5021 Agency Distributors 13Center
324-5256 Ager Teresa Mrs 14Fish
672-0200 Ager Wallace 36Center
324-0176 Agid Eric 120HarvestDr
672-0011 Aging Agency 12Main
324-0308 Agins Jon C MD 10Ford
489-5847 –If No Answer Call
417-5121 Aglione Joseph 24State
672-0275 Aglow Beauty Salon 3Main
324-0131 Agoglia F M 12RogersPl
324-0056 Agostini Alberto 7Maxwell
417-5629 Agranott Louis 16Jordan
417-5228 Agrant Priscilla 12Church
324-5013 Agrin David 15Hardy
672-0103 Aguero Raul 47Main
324-5858 Aguero Victor 31Summer
672-5650 Aguirre Calvin 70E4
489-5787 Ah Nong Chen 17Eagle
489-0165 Aharoyan Arch 14Elm
489-5320 Ahart Ernest 31Maple
672-5405 Ahearn Homer T 13W2
417-5703 Ahearn William 7Adams
324-5109 Ahearne William 41Hardy
489-5492 Ahern Steven 4DarkRiverRd
672-5433 AHF FUNERAL HOME 12Center
417-5312 Ahlers Clifton 31Jordan
324-0351 Ahmad Mohammed 4Maxwell
324-5241 Ahrendt Hans 14Ford
672-0001 Ahrens David 13Main
672-5111 AID EMERGENCY SERVICE INC
        2Center
324-5441 Aid Lawrence 7Fish
672-5669 Aida's Restaurant 4W14
672-5806 Aides Incorporated 13NMain
324-5331 Aiken Collins 7ParkAv
417-5671 Aiken Martin P 12State
489-0123 Aikens Larry 23HoustonRd
672-5716 Aikido Martial Arts 14E2
672-5986 Aim-2-Please Market 7Center

20

Is it a good idea to use your fingers when reading? Most teachers say *no*. In the early grades, children are taught that their eyes are not on their fingertips. Fingers can't read. Pointing at words as you read them usually just slows you down.

But sometimes your fingertips do come in handy. At these times you move your fingers down—*not across*—the page. Fingers are useful for dictionary work. They also help in finding phone numbers. Your fingertips seem to pull your eyes down the list of names faster. You are not as tempted to stop and read before you reach the right spot.

Letters can be your "keys" when skimming an alphabetical listing like a phone-book page. Suppose you were looking for Pat Agatielli's address. You would move your eyes and fingertips very quickly until you came to names beginning with *Ag*. These letters would be your signal to start reading the list more carefully. ▪

SKILL BUILDER 4

Directions: Look for a moment at the opposite page. Let your eyes wander here and there. Then answer the questions below. For the phone-book page, use your free hand, not the one you write with. First, find the section of names you need to look at closely to answer each question—the *Ad*s, for instance, or the *Ag*s. Let your fingers do the running as your eyes follow. Keep a finger on the answer if you have to write it down. Work as fast as you can.

1. Is there an Adult-Youth League in the community? (yes or no)

   _____

2. What is the number of Linda Agate?

   _____

3. If you needed the Aid Emergency Service in a hurry, you should dial

   _____

4. If told to call Bill Abbott, why might you have trouble?

   _____

5. What is the street address of the Adroit Cleaners?

   _____

6. Can we be sure that there is a Frank Agoglia in the phone book? (yes or no)

   _____

7. What is the number of William Ahearne?

   _____

8. Does Eric Agid live on Harvest Drive? (yes or no)

   _____

9. Does Milton Ackerman have a listed number? (yes or no)

   _____

10. What is the home address of Dr. Bernard Adorno?

   _____

Finding Stories
You Want to Read

CONTENTS

iii

On the opposite page is a table of contents. It comes from a book of short stories. It will tell you if a particular story is in the book. It will help you with page numbers. It will also help you choose a story to read. You can often tell from the titles which story may interest you.

Suppose your purpose was to find a good ghost story. You certainly wouldn't have to read the whole contents page. Instead, you would skim the titles for key words like *ghost, phantom, grave,* and *horror.* ■

SKILL BUILDER 5

Directions: Find the story that is about the topic in column I. Write its title in column II. Write the number of the page on which it begins in column III. The first one has been done for you.

I THE STORY ABOUT	II IS ENTITLED	III ON PAGE
1. Little people	*Among the Dwarfs*	*2*
2. Life in the Far North		
3. Powerful animals		
4. Life in the West		
5. A ghost		
6. A pirate		
7. An airplane pilot		
8. A Sioux		
9. A railroad wreck		
10. A blind person		

Now write the titles you didn't use on the lines below. Tell what you think each *might* be about.

1. *"The Stolen Bag"- a boy's inner troubles when he finds $10,000.*

2. _____

3. _____

4. _____

5. _____

Skimming an Index

423

◆   What would you do if you wanted to find a certain subject or the name of a certain person in a book? To save time, you would look for an *index* at the back of the book. An index is an alphabetical list with page numbers of topics and people.

Skimming through the index would be the easiest way to find what you want quickly. If you were looking for a person, her or his last name would be your key word. If you were looking for a topic, words having to do with that topic would be your keys. For instance, if your topic was farming, *agriculture* would be a key word. The words *farming* and *agriculture* have about the same meaning.   ■

SKILL BUILDER 6

Directions: Answer the following questions by skimming the index on page 12. Use your fingers on the index page for added speed.

1. From what kind of a book does this index seem to come? _____

2. On what pages will you find information on farming? _____

3. Does the index list Clara Barton? _____

4. Does the index list Louisa May Alcott? _____

5. Which pages tell about China since World War II? _____

6. Which pages contain information on cars? _____

7. Which page would tell you who George Rogers Clark was? _____

8. Which item in the index is probably a title? _____

9. On what page might the picture below be found? _____

10. What key word might help you find information about education? _____

Two Halves Make a Whole

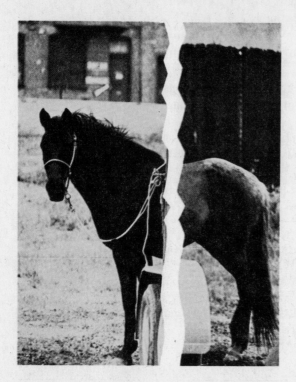

▶ Do you get the picture? However you look at it, it's a horse. You knew it was a horse by seeing the two halves as single units and then putting them together. You didn't have to look at each ear, each eye, each hoof, and so on. You put them together at a glance, and your mind said *horse*.

It's much the same with reading. To read with speed, you have to see groups of words as single units. If you want to read rapidly, try to group words together so that they "flash in your mind" all at once. ▪

SKILL BUILDER 7

Directions: Draw a line from the first part of each sentence to the second part that makes the most sense. Try to take in each sentence part at a single glance.

FIRST PART	SECOND PART
1. Sometimes half the picture	increase your reading speed.
2. The same is true	doesn't tell the whole story.
3. Matching sentence parts helps to	many words at once.
4. Your eyes are forced to skim over	thoughts out of half-sentences.
5. You have to make whole	with sentences.

Check: Read all of your finished sentences in order. Do they all sound right to you?

SKILL BUILDER 8

Directions: On the line provided, copy the second part that best completes each sentence.

FIRST PART | SECOND PART

1. Did you ever see a horse _____   do _not_ make a whole.

2. The photo was taken _____   could do in a race.

3. Think of what this horse _____   third by a tail.

4. Its back is big enough _____   guessed the truth.

5. It could both _____   course, two horses in the picture.

6. It could take _____   win and tie for second.

7. By now you've probably _____   for three jockeys.

8. There are, of _____   as long as this one?

9. That's only _____   near Baltimore, Maryland.

10. _These_ two halves _____   horse sense.

Spotting Words
That Go Together

▶ Add the numbers below. Work as fast as you can.

$$0 + 2 + 1 + 3 + 3 + 1 + 2 + 1 = \underline{\qquad}$$
$$(2 + 4) + (4 + 3) = \underline{\qquad}$$
$$6 + 7 = \underline{\qquad}$$

Now read the following two sentences. Which is easier to understand?

| My | brother | is | going | to | New | York | next | week. |

My brother   is going   to New York   next week.

What did you discover? You probably found that adding two or four numbers is faster and easier than adding eight numbers. Reading words in groups is faster and easier than reading each word separately.

If you're like most people, you have a lot of reading to do. Seeing words as groups helps you read more quickly and with better understanding. Think of words as pieces of a puzzle. If you group pieces together, you can see the whole picture more clearly. ▪

SKILL BUILDER 9

Directions: Reading by word groups is an important skill. Prove this to yourself by reading the two paragraphs below. First, read the one on the left. Let your eyes rest on each word before moving on to the next. Then read the second paragraph. See the words as groups. Write a short explanation below of why the second paragraph is easier to read.

THE LANTERN FLY

The lantern fly is one of nature's freaks. It lives in the jungles of South America. To protect itself from birds, it has a false head that looks like an alligator's. (Most birds are afraid of alligators, even small ones.) The false head has two blind eyes with tiny white dots in them. The long snout is the shape of an alligator's. On its side are rows of white marks that look just like teeth.

THE LANTERN FLY

The lantern fly is one **of nature's freaks.** It lives **in the jungles** of South America. **To protect itself** from birds, **it has** a false head **that looks** like an alligator's. **(Most birds** are afraid **of alligators,** even small ones.) **The false head** has two blind eyes **with tiny white dots** in them. **The long snout** is the shape **of an alligator's.** On its sides **are rows** of white marks **that look** just like teeth.

Explanation: _____

_____

_____

SKILL BUILDER 10

Directions: The word groups on each line below will make a good sentence if put in the right order. In the blank before each group of words, write the number of the place that group will occupy in the sentence. For instance, the numbers for the first would be 2-3-1 because the sentence would read *The state police had found the stolen money.*

1. _2_ had found   _3_ the stolen money   _1_ the state police

2. ___ bright red   ___ was once painted   ___ that little house

3. ___ my friend Jill   ___ our class president   ___ was elected

4. ___ use less gas   ___ than older ones   ___ most new cars

5. ___ I didn't know   ___ how to do it   ___ that you knew

6. ___ growing heavier   ___ seems to be   ___ Helen's grandfather

7. ___ my little sister   ___ than I do   ___ eats more

8. ___ failed the test   ___ of the students   ___ nearly a third

9. ___ a day   ___ Mr. Samuels eats   ___ three meals

10. ___ I wouldn't call   ___ a hard one   ___ this exercise

SKILL BUILDER 11

Directions: Below are ten questions. They can be answered by looking at the road signs on the next page. Read the first question. Then turn the page and skim the signs for the correct answer. Do not try to read every word. On the line before each question, write the letter of the sign that gives the answer. Do one question at a time.

_____ 1. How far is it to Claryville?

_____ 2. Where is Route 7 closed?

_____ 3. For what speed are the lights set?

_____ 4. How do you get onto Route 8 North?

_____ 5. In which direction must you pay a toll?

_____ 6. How far is it to food and fuel?

_____ 7. What is the clearance of the low bridge ahead?

_____ 8. Which route should you take for Hopkinton?

_____ 9. During what hours must traffic stay in a single lane?

_____ 10. Who or what does one sign say is at work?

(A) TAKE 202 FOR SCENIC ROUTE

(B) CLARYVILLE 20 MILES

(C) LIGHTS SET FOR 30 MPH SPEED

(D) LOW BRIDGE AHEAD CLEARANCE 11 FEET

(E) PAY TOLL GOING EAST ONLY

(F) Food and Fuel 5 Miles

(G) FOR HOPKINTON TAKE ROUTE 95

(H) ROUTE 7 CLOSED NORTH OF DANBURY

(I) ONE LANE TRAFFIC 4 - 6 P.M.

(J) YOUR HIGHWAY TAX DOLLARS AT WORK

(K) TAKE SECOND RIGHT FOR 8 NORTH

(L) Welcome To Riverton

(M) AIRPORT AHEAD NO STOPPING ON HIGHWAY

Take Your Pick

▶ Once again, your purpose here is to gain speed by seeing groups of words as single units. The modified cloze exercise below will help you with this skill. ▪

SKILL BUILDER 12

Directions: In each sentence below, circle the word groups in **heavy black type** that make the most sense.

1. When Mrs. Horton was **a boy,** she played soccer in the fall and softball **in the river.**
                            a girl,   **in the spring.**

2. The three men loaded **the white cloud** before they took time off **to eat lunch.**
                            the large truck   **to work harder.**

3. In the zoo the children saw **four racing cars** that should have had their **diapers changed.**
              three scrawny camels   **roots checked.**
                 two busy teachers   **pen cleaned up.**

4. The foolish king **taxed his people** unwisely until it was **sky high.**
                spent his money   **city air.**
                killed his enemies   **all gone.**

5. **To catch the thief,** the police sent the fingerprints to Washington, D.C., **for the President.**
      To prevent accidents,   **by airmail.**
      To find the money,   **in a large box.**

6. **Running rapidly,** the half-grown puppy charged **under its crib clumsily.**
      Driving a car,   **down the street.**
      Tapping a cane,   **into its helicopter.**

7. Running to first base, Libby **let the ball** go **between the goalposts.**
                saw the ball   **into the hoop.**
                let herself   **over the fence.**

8. "Gimme a cookie," **thundered the boss** in the high chair **under and over.**
               ordered the guard   **over and over.**
               whined the child   **over and under.**

9. **Pale and sad,** Carmella lay in bed **with a temperature** for the first time in her life.
      Glowing with health,   **with a picnic**
      Standing up straight,   **with a fever**

10. **Have you heard** the old saying about **going fishing** for a rainy day?
       You have heard   **buying presents**
       Are you sure   **saving money**

Skimming for the "Who/What"

▶ A sentence, of course, is made of words. But just as important, a sentence is made of groups of words. Seeing these *groups* as *thought units* helps you if your purpose is to read rapidly.

Groups of words do different things in a sentence. One group might tell *when* the action happened. Another might tell *where* something occurred. Still another might tell *who* or *what* the sentence is about. The words that tell *who* or *what* are probably the most important in a sentence. They are called the SUBJECT of the sentence.

Look closely at the sentences below. The words that tell *who* or *what* each sentence is about are in **heavy black type.** Notice that these words usually come at the beginning of a sentence. Notice, too, that they can sometimes be found in the middle of a sentence, or even at the end. ▪

Two young campers were lost in the woods with only one match.
Their whole lives depended on that one match.
Several pieces of firewood lay neatly piled on the ground.
The last match was lighted under the wood.
Up in flames went **the wood,** to the campers' great delight.
Into a brook fell **one of the campers.**
In a minute **the smiling camper** came up with a pocket full of fish to cook for dinner.

SKILL BUILDER 13

Directions: Underline the word or word group that tells *who* or *what* each sentence is about. Work as fast as you can.

1. People in the United States watch a lot of TV.

2. Some TV sets are on nearly all the time.

3. The average TV set is on about six hours a day.

4. Many boys and girls watch TV too much.

5. The average 18 year old has watched about 15,000 hours of TV.

6. He or she has spent only 13,000 hours in school.

7. Reading and writing now take up less and less time.

8. Reading scores go down and down.

9. Down and down go reading scores.

10. Anyone who really wants to can improve, however.

SKILL BUILDER 14

Directions: Here is another modified cloze exercise. First, read the selection all the way through. Then go back and circle the word group that belongs in each blank.

RATTLESNAKE HUNTS

Rattlesnake hunts take place in many states. __1__, however, are in Texas and Oklahoma. In those states, both men and women enjoy the sport. Sometimes even __2__ join in. __3__ first has to find a rattler. Then he or she picks it up with long tongs. __4__ is then carried to the "pit," or hole. Soon __5__ are squirming around together in the hole. If __6__ gets bitten, good care is right at hand. When __7__ is over, the snakes' heads are chopped off.

__8__ tastes something like chicken or fish. Its price is high. __9__ on the tail also bring good prices.

__10__ object to snake hunts. But the sport *does* get rid of rattlers. And so far there are still plenty of rattlers left.

1. None of them
   Most of them
   All of them

2. healthy women
   the rattlesnakes
   young children

3. A hunter
   All the hunters
   A certain woman

4. The injured hunter
   The poisonous snake
   One of the tongs

5. all the kids
   the dead creatures
   hundreds of snakes

6. one of the hunters
   a woman
   a man

7. the dawn
   the blood
   the hunt

8. Rattlesnake meat
   A snakeskin
   He or she

9. The eyes
   The rattles
   Some diamonds

10. Good rattlesnake hunters
    Some animal lovers
    Most snakes

Skimming for "Does/Is"

▶ Most sentences have two important groups of words. One group tells *who* or *what* the sentence is about. The other group tells what the "who/what" *does* or *is*. Try to see both the "who/what" and "does/is" groups as thought units. This skill will help you if your purpose is to read with speed and understanding.

In some sentences, of course, the "who/what" and the "does/is" are single words. But usually they are word groups. Let your eye run down the sentences below. How far can you go and still see both parts as word groups? ▪

WHO/WHAT	DOES/IS
Saws	cut.
Carpenters' saws	cut wood
The carpenters' saws	cut the wood.
The carpenters' sharp saws	cut the hard wood.
The carpenters' sharp new saws	can cut the hard knotty wood.
The three carpenters' sharp new saws	can cut through the hard knotty wood.
Ann	is cold.
Poor Ann	is very cold.
Poor little Ann	is very cold and tired.
My poor little Ann	is very cold and too tired.
My poor little girl Ann	is very cold and much too tired.
My poor little girl Annabel	is very cold and much too tired out.

SKILL BUILDER 15

Directions: Underline the "does/is" word group in each sentence. Work quickly. Try to see the word groups as thought units, not as rows of single words.

1. Hang gliding is a popular sport.

2. The flier hangs under a huge kite.

3. She or he holds onto a metal bar.

4. The flier tilts the kite with the bar.

5. The tilt of the kite controls direction.

6. A rising wind is necessary to take off.

7. The flier jumps off into the breeze.

8. Rising air currents, or "thermals," carry the flier up.

9. Some hang gliders fly over a mile high.

10. Tricky winds can make hang gliding dangerous.

▶ The action or state of being told about in the "does/is" part of a sentence need not happen in the present. It can happen in the past, with terms like *was, were, went, had gone,* and *did go* showing past time. It can also happen in the future, with terms like *will be, will go,* and *shall have gone* showing future time. ■

SKILL BUILDER 16

Directions: Underline the "does/is" word group in each sentence that follows. Then place a P (past) or an F (future) on the line in front of the numeral.

_____ 1. Thirty-six people were killed hang gliding in 1974.

_____ 2. That year was the worst year.

_____ 3. Safety will improve in coming years.

_____ 4. Some people have always liked risky sports.

_____ 5. Years ago, mountain climbing killed many people.

_____ 6. Then motorcycle racing, skydiving, and hang gliding grew popular.

_____ 7. Scuba diving added its toll.

_____ 8. Next year risky sports will take about 10,000 lives.

_____ 9. But in spite of the danger, in coming years risky sports will continue to grow.

_____ 10. More and more people will demand thrills.

Skimming for the "When"

▶ First, look back at page 23. There you learned that "does/is" word groups also say something about *when*.

Present time: I *go*. I *am going*. I *am* here now.
Past time: I *went*. I *have gone*. I *was* here. I *have been* here.
Future time: I *will go*. I *will have gone*. I *shall be* here. I *shall have been* here.

But sometimes other words are needed to "tell the time" in a sentence. These can be single words like *yesterday, today, tomorrow, Tuesday, sometimes,* and *always.* They can also be word groups like *next week, in the future,* or *long ago.* Seeing these "when" words as groups, or thought units, will help you read faster and better.

Quickly skim the sentences that follow. Try to see the words in **heavy black type** as groups, not as single words. ▪

A hundred years ago, most students went to one-room country schools.
The schools **very often** had two terms.
The older boys went to school **during the winter.**
For about three months, they were taught by a man.
The teacher had to get up **early in the morning** to make a fire in a wood stove.
But **in the spring** the older boys were needed for farm work.
When they began work, the girls and small children began school.
A woman teacher began the new term **after spring planting began.**
The "spring term" often lasted **all summer long.**
At that time teachers got about $5.00 to $7.00 for a week's work.

SKILL BUILDER 17

Directions: Underline the word group in each sentence that tells *when.* Work as fast as you can.

1. Two hundred years ago, many children didn't go to school at all.

2. Before 1800 most schools were crude log cabins.

3. Teachers in those days got $1.00 or less a week.

4. Frequently but not always they "boarded around" at the homes of their students.

5. Many towns could not afford to pay the whole school bill during this period.

6. When the money ran out, the parents had to pay.

7. The parents would support the school until the end of the year.

8. Total costs back in those days were about a penny per student per day.

9. Older girls who had been in school for several years helped the teacher.

10. Small groups of students read aloud while others studied.

SKILL BUILDER 18

Directions: In each sentence, two word groups appear in **heavy black type.** Try to read each of these groups at a single glance. Then underline the one that tells *when.* Work as fast as you can.

since the old days.
1. Schools have changed a great deal
in some of our cities.

_____

Tell us, please,
2.   do we have eight or more grades in one room?
In our time,

_____

standing up together?
3. Do small groups of students recite
at the same time?

_____

as other classes study?
4. Does the teacher work with some classes
more than others?

_____

for hours at a time
5. Do students sit   on benches with no backs?
so uncomfortably

_____

Yes or no,
6.   have you written on a slate because paper cost too much?
In your life,

_____

for the better.
7. Schools are changing
all the time.

_____

during your school years?
8. What changes have you noticed
in your particular school?

_____

With more money
9.   there will be even more changes.
In future years

_____

with many more computers?
10. Who knows what schools will be like
a hundred years from now?

Skimming for the "Where"

WHO/WHAT	DOES/IS	WHEN	?
Most of us	see cans and bottles	too often	by the roadside.

▶ What word belongs in the box? The word WHERE, of course. Some groups of words tell *who* or *what* a sentence is about. Other groups tell what the "who/what" *does* or *is*. Others answer the question *when?* And still others answer the question *where?* If you want to read with rapid understanding, seeing these word groups as thought units will help you.

Take a look at the sentences that follow. The word groups in **heavy black type** all tell *where*. Try to see them as groups, not as single words. ▪

There are many stories of people who disappeared **into thin air.**
But one of these people once returned **to the land of the living.**
This true story happened **in Newark, New Jersey,** about ten years ago.
A confused Bruce Burkan found himself sitting **on a bench.**
He was, he saw, **in a bus station.**
Suddenly he looked **down at his clothes.**
Nowhere on earth had he ever seen the cheap blue suit before.

SKILL BUILDER 19

Directions: Underline the word group that tells *where* in each sentence. Seeing these words as a group will help you work faster.

1. Nineteen-year-old Bruce Burkan couldn't remember where he'd been.

2. In a wallet he found no bills and only seven cents.

3. He quickly got up and walked across the room.

4. At a newsstand he learned the date.

5. The last thing he remembered was going to a beach with his girl friend two months earlier.

6. The beach was at Asbury Park, New Jersey.

7. He and his girl friend had been sunning themselves on the sand.

8. He had suddenly thought of the parking meter next to his car.

9. To the parking lot he had hurried with the necessary coins.

10. That was the last place he remembered being.

SKILL BUILDER 20

Directions: Two word groups in each sentence are printed in **heavy black type.** Try to read each of these groups at a single glance. Then underline the one that gives the "where" of the sentence. Work as fast as you can.

1. Bruce's girl friend had waited a long time and had finally gone **to the parking lot.**
   ahead and cried.

2. **After a moment spent looking,**
   she found the car.
   Right where they had parked it,

3. It was locked, and there was no sign of Bruce **that she could see.**
   anywhere she looked.

4. Soon newspapers and radios carried the strange story **about Bruce Burkan.**
   all over the state.

5. But nobody was able to say **where** Bruce was.
   how

6. His family looked **and advertised for him,** and finally they held a memorial
   everywhere they could,
   service for him.

7. Then Bruce suddenly "came to life" **in the bus station.**
   looking just fine.

8. He had total amnesia, or loss of memory, about **the two months.**
   where he'd been.

9. He had probably traveled **for the time** under another name.
   here and there

10. But with the newspaper stories and all the red hair **on his head,** why had
    that went uncut,
    no one recognized him?

Skimming for the "How" and "Why"

▶ Word groups in sentences do different things. Some groups tell *how* something happens or *how* something should be done: You can improve your reading speed **by reading word groups.** The groups in **heavy black type** below all tell *how*. ▪

Read the following advice **quickly.**
But don't read **too rapidly.**
Don't read **so fast that you'll forget.**
Imagine you were struggling **like mad** in water over your head.
Is there a way to save your life **calmly?**

SKILL BUILDER 21

Directions: In the sentences below, try to read each numbered part as a word group. Write the number of the part that tells *how* in the blank before each sentence. The first one has been done for you.

          1   2   3

__3__   **1.** You   can save your life   with the "survival float."

          1   2   3

_____   **2.** The human body   can float   like a cork in water.

          1   2   3

_____   **3.** But the body   will only float   with lungs full of air.

          1   2   3

_____   **4.** Floating face down,   the body   is quite comfortable.

          1   2   3

_____   **5.** Don't thrash your arms about   every which way   in an emergency.

          1   2   3

_____   **6.** Just take a deep breath   and let your body sink,   staying as relaxed as you can.

          1   2

_____   **7.** Do this   as shown above.

          1   2   3   4

_____   **8.** Push down   slowly and easily   when your body   stops sinking.

          1   2

_____   **9.** Push down   with your arms and legs.

          1   2   3

_____   **10.** Then,   by raising your chin,   you can take another deep breath.

▶ There is one more kind of word group to learn about. Groups of this kind answer the question *why?* They give a *reason* for something else in the sentence. ▪

The "survival float" was invented **to save lives.**

The "survival float" was invented **because 7,000 people drown each year.**

The human body floats in water **because it's lighter than water.**

Since it's lighter, the human body will float in water.

To stay alive, learn the "survival float."

Practice it **so you'll never drown.**

SKILL BUILDER 22

Directions: Two word groups in each sentence are printed in **heavy black type.** Try to read each of these groups at a single glance. Then underline the one that tells *why.* Work as fast as you can.

To avoid danger,
1.   practice the "survival float" in water only armpit high.
Sometime soon,

_____

Outdoors or indoors,
2.   the "survival float" can be learned in a short time.
Since it's easy,

_____

                and later been thankful.
3. Many people have saved their lives
                because they practiced it.

_____

                because he knew it.
4. A sailor once survived for five hours
                in very icy water.

_____

Remember this simple rule:
5.   tilt your body in the direction you want to go.
To move through the water,

Go on to the next page. →

SKILL BUILDER 23

Directions: Sometimes it's hard to tell the difference between the "how" and the "why." Read each sentence below. Then decide whether the word group in **heavy black type** tells *how* or *why*. Circle the correct word that follows the sentence.

1. **Since it's important,** start "survival-float" practice soon.   HOW   WHY

2. Do this **by timing your breathing.**   HOW   WHY

3. You'll need a watch with a second hand **to time yourself.**   HOW   WHY

4. Breathe **deeply but quickly** while looking at the watch.   HOW   WHY

5. You may have trouble at first **because you'll be nervous.**   HOW   WHY

6. Try to feel comfortable **with ten seconds between breaths.**   HOW   WHY

7. **By lying down,** you can relax completely.   HOW   WHY

8. Then forget the watch, keep breathing, and lie **on your stomach.**   HOW   WHY

9. Imagine you are moving in the water **as shown in the drawings.**   HOW   WHY

10. Do this every week or so **to remind yourself.**   HOW   WHY

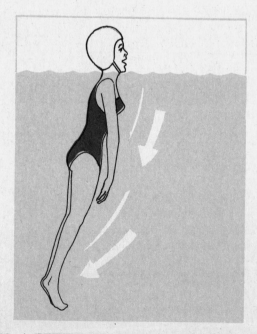
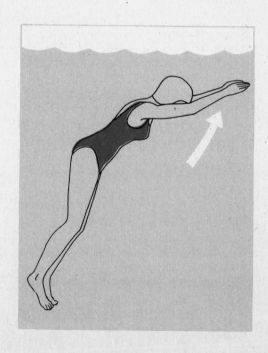

Sharpening Your Sentence Sense

▶ Good readers are not word-by-word readers. Instead, they read by word groups. Some groups of words tell *who* or *what* a sentence is about. Other groups tell what the "who/what" *does* or *is*. Still other groups tell *when, where, how,* or *why.* If you want to read with speed and understanding, remember to read by word groups. ■

SKILL BUILDER 24

Directions: Read each sentence below as fast as you can. Then look at the word group in **heavy black type.** Circle the word after the sentence that tells what this group does in the sentence.

1. **Alan and Tinka** got to Angel's party before I did. WHERE WHY DOES WHO

2. Hold the bat **at the very end** to get long hits. IS WHEN HOW WHAT

3. **In the 1940s** a U.S. worker could buy a new car for $1,000. WHAT DOES HOW WHEN

4. **Bus passes** will be available in the main office after lunch. WHO IS WHERE WHAT

5. Our new TV set **works well.** DOES WHO WHAT WHERE

6. The keys are kept on the table **in the hall.** IS WHEN WHERE HOW

7. Alison studies five nights a week **to get good marks.** WHO WHAT WHEN WHY

8. These days everything I buy **is expensive.** WHERE IS DOES WHO

9. Hector hasn't been to school all week **because he's sick.** WHAT WHY HOW WHO

10. Alan and Tinka got to Angel's party **before I did.** WHEN IS WHAT HOW

11. Hold the bat at the very end **to get long hits.** DOES WHY WHO WHERE

12. In the 1940s **a U.S. worker** could buy a new car for $1,000. WHO WHAT WHY DOES

13. Bus passes will be available in the main office **after lunch.** WHO WHAT WHEN IS

14. **Our new TV set** works well. WHO WHAT DOES WHEN

15. **The keys** are kept on the table in the hall. WHAT WHO DOES WHERE

16. Alison studies **five nights a week** to get good marks. WHO WHAT WHEN WHY

17. **These days** everything I buy is expensive. WHAT WHERE IS WHEN

18. Hector hasn't been to school **all week** because he's sick. WHY WHEN DOES HOW

19. Bus passes will be available **in the main office** after lunch. WHO WHAT WHERE WHEN

20. There are 20 sentences, and this one **is the last.** WHAT DOES WHY IS

③ APPLYING YOUR SKIMMING SKILLS

Reading With a Hop, Skip, and Jump

▶ The way you read always depends on your purpose in reading. Sometimes it's not important to remember every fact. It's enough to get the general idea.

How do you read quickly and still get the general idea? The best way is to read only the *important* words. You can almost skip over the other words. That is the right way to read with a hop, skip, and jump. That is what is usually meant by skimming.

Remember, it's not good to read all selections this way. If a selection is at all important for you, it's better to read carefully. But here your purpose is to read rapidly, with the help of important words. ▪

SKILL BUILDER 25

Directions: The important words here are printed in **heavy black type.** Let your eyes rest on these words as you read. Skim over the other words. Read the selection only once. Then read the ten sentences that follow the selection. Circle the letter of the word or words that correctly complete each one. Try not to look back at the selection.

THE PRICE OF WATER

You **go** to the **faucet** in your **kitchen.** You **flip** it **open.** Out **comes** a **gush** of **water, all** you **want.** You can **drink** it or use it to **cook.** You can **wash** things. **No one** sets any **limit** on **how much** you use. It is **free,** like the **air.** But that is **not quite true.** It is **not really** free. It **only seems** to be **free.**

Suppose you were **walking** on a **country road** in the **summer.** You might see some **berries** growing on bushes. Those berries **would be free.** But if you live **in the city** and **want** some **berries,** you **must pay. Why?** Someone had to **pick** them. Someone had to **pack** them. Someone had to **bring** them to the city **by truck.** A **store** had to **sell** them. **Much work** was **done** to bring them to you. That **work** has to be **paid** for.

In the **country**, too, you might **see** a **brook.** You might **drink** from it. That **water** would be **free.** But if you **lived** a **mile away** from the water, you would have to **walk back and forth, carrying pails.** Or you would **pay someone** to **do that work** for you. Then the **water** would **no longer** be **free.**

What happens when you **turn** on a **faucet** in the **city?** The **water comes** to you **from** a great **distance.** It **may be** from a **reservoir** more than 50 **miles** (81 km) away. **Think** of all the **work** this took. It took **years** of **planning** and **building.** It took **thousands** of **workers.** It took **miles** and miles of **pipeline.** Now it takes **constant care** to **keep** the water **fresh** and **pure.**

All this **work** has to be **paid for.** The **whole city pays** through **taxes.** You may **live** in an **apartment.** But you **still pay.** Your **landlord pays water taxes** every year. Your landlord makes these **taxes part of** your **rent.** It's really **you** who must **pay** for the **water.**

No, **water** is **not free.** Yet we **don't mind** the **small price we pay** for it. For **without** pure **water** we **could not live.**

1. The selection is mainly about

   (A) berries.   (B) water.   (C) taxes.

2. The selection refers to

   (A) the city only.   (B) the country only.   (C) both city and country.

3. In most homes, water

   (A) is free.   (B) only seems free.   (C) costs much too much.

4. Berries along a country road are

   (A) free.   (B) poisonous.   (C) covered with dust.

5. A general idea in the selection is that people pay for

   (A) their mistakes.   (B) nothing.   (C) work done.

6. In general, the selection tells about water's

   (A) purity.   (B) freshness.   (C) price.

7. Most city water comes from

   (A) nearby wells.   (B) rivers.   (C) great distances.

8. Landlords

   (A) pay water taxes.   (B) get their own water free.   (C) work too hard.

9. We're lucky to have

   (A) free water.   (B) pure water.   (C) hot water.

10. The selection does *not* mention

   (A) hard and soft water.   (B) reservoirs and pipelines.   (C) uses of water.

The Magic of Spot Words

▶ This lesson will show you a new way to remember what you read.

Suppose you have to read something for a school test. It doesn't interest you very much. But you have to learn the information it gives. What's the best way to hold the facts in your mind?

When you start to study, have a pencil and a piece of paper at hand. Then, first, read the selection with care. Second, skim the selection for SPOT WORDS and jot them down. Spot words are those few terms that will help you recall the rest. And third, read the spot words over to yourself. They should bring everything else you've read back to mind.

Read the selection below. On the right are some spot words. When you finish, cover the selection with your hand. *Read just the spot words.* As you read each one, a complete idea will flash across your mind. ▪

THE LOTTERY RIP-OFF

Many states now have lotteries. You buy a ticket, and you take your chances. But your chances are very, very poor.

"Bet with your head, not over it," advises one state. That's nonsense! A person who bets with his or her head wouldn't bet at all. Let's take New York as an example. Suppose $100 worth of tickets are bought. Out of that money, only $40 is returned to the people who bought the tickets. The state keeps $45. The rest of the money pays for running the lottery itself.

What kind of odds are those? The state keeps much more money than it pays the winners. Even at a racetrack, the winners get a better break. Tracks pay back about $82 for every $100 bet.

lotteries
poor
with head

New York
$100
$40 returned
$45 state

racetrack
$82

SKILL BUILDER 26

Directions: On page 35 is a selection from a textbook. Read it carefully. Then skim it for spot words. Write these words on the lines at the right. Finally, *read just the spot words.* Each one should bring to mind a complete idea. When you finish, underline the choice that correctly completes each sentence at the bottom of the page.

People didn't always speak. Long ago, they had no language. At some point, language must have been invented.

How was language invented? No one is sure. Experts give us only theories, or ideas. Here are six of them:

1. *The ding-dong theory.* The first human words sounded like the things they meant. A bell, of course, sounds like "ding-dong." Suppose an early human once dropped a stone in the water. He or she might have heard "splash" and then said "splash."

2. *The bow-wow theory.* Animals make noises: "meow," "bow-wow," "moo," *etc.* Today these animal noises are human words. Our first words might have been copies of animal sounds.

3. *The pooh-pooh theory.* Excited or angry people often speak without thinking. Suppose someone once bit into a piece of meat. It was tough, and the person got mad. She or he might have said "pooh-pooh" to mean "that's no good."

4. *The ta-rah-rah theory.* Small children make up nonsense words. They say or sing them when they're happy. In the same way, early people might have made up words with no meanings. Then the words began to mean something. "Tah-rah-rah," for instance, might have come to mean "party," "sing," or "fire."

5. *The yo-heave-ho theory.* All heavy work once had to be done by people working together. These groups often made noises to keep in time. For instance, sailors once said "yo-heave-ho" as they pulled on ropes. Sounds like these might have been the first words.

6. *The itty-bitty theory.* This is not an easy theory to understand. Each word-sound is made with the mouth in a certain position. Sometimes this position is like what the word means. Think, for instance, about the word "long." You make a *long* tube of the mouth. Now say "little," "itty-bitty," and "teeny-weeny." You force air through an *itty-bitty* opening above the tongue.

Which theory do you like best? Maybe you don't see much sense in any of them. If so, you may be right. It could be that none of the six theories is correct.

1. The selection is about the (limits, invention) of language.

2. A theory is an (agreement, idea) about something.

3. The word *pop*—hear it?—is an example of the (yo-heave-ho, ding-dong) theory.

4. The bow-wow theory suggests that human words came from (anger, animals).

5. An example of the itty-bitty theory is the word (*long*, *fine*).

6. Sailors pulling on ropes together once said ("yo-heave-ho," "ta-rah-rah").

7. Children's nonsense words suggest the (yo-heave-ho, ta-rah-rah) theory.

8. The pooh-pooh theory might also be called the (ouch, cow) theory.

9. Experts have come up with at least (six, ten) different theories.

10. It could be that all of the theories are (correct, wrong).

Looking for Answers

▶ Using spot words is a helpful study skill. Here's another skill you may have discovered for yourself: Read the questions on the selection first, and then read to answer the questions. There's nothing wrong with this practice. In fact, some books give you the questions first to guide your reading. ▪

SKILL BUILDER 27

Directions: Look at the first question on the opposite page. Then skim the selection below with the question in mind. Read only enough to find the answer. Write it down, and go on to the next question.

YOUTHFUL AMBITION

(1) When I was young, I had a secret ambition. No, I never told anyone about it. Sometimes at school we used to talk about careers. I lied and lied. But I never felt bad about it. Knowing how to lie was all part of my plan.

(2) I wanted to be a police detective. I guess I'd seen too many detectives in the movies and on TV. They were tough and tricky. They led glamorous lives. They lied for good reasons. Their whole lives were lies. Every week would bring a new case—and a new adventure.

(3) Of course, other aims sometimes entered my mind. But they never lasted long. Once I planned to run away and join a circus. That dream went away in a week. Another time my goal was to drive my own taxi. And later I thought about being a salesperson. I would start on the sidewalk and end with million-dollar deals. After all, a good salesperson can sell anything.

(4) But I always came back to the detective idea. I'd have a special power over life and death. I'd be able to put on different clothes and become different people. One day I'd dress like a bum. The next I'd be a college professor. I used to dream of people looking at me on the street. Their sidelong glances asked silent questions. They wondered about me.

(5) And then there would be days when I didn't wear a disguise. I could be myself. I'd put on a cool, bored look. I'd walk into my office like a big, ugly bear. I'd speak in grunts. Everyone else would smile and say, "Hi there, Lt. Ringo." Sometimes I used to practice that bored look in front of a mirror. I'd pretend not to have a care in the world. Look at those steely eyes! The world knew better than to mess with *me*.

(6) One dream kept coming back to me. I'd come upon a big holdup. It would usually be in a bank. I'd be in plain clothes and off duty. There would be four or five robbers. I'd get behind two of them and knock their heads together. They'd fall to the floor. Then I'd bluff the others. They'd surrender. The bank manager, still shaking, would come forward. "It was nothing at all," I'd say with a shrug. "I only did my duty."

1. Why didn't the writer of the selection feel bad about lying during talks about careers?

_____

2. What did movies and TV have to do with the career plan?

_____

3. What was one thing about a police detective's life that the writer liked?

_____

4. What were three other careers the writer thought of for short periods of time?

_____

5. What are two words in paragraph 3 that mean "desire to become something"?

_____

6. What two kinds of disguises did the writer dream of wearing?

_____

7. How did the writer imagine he or she would look in real life as a police detective?

_____

8. What did the writer do to try to develop this look?

_____

9. In the dream of the bank holdup, how were the robbers caught?

_____

10. What would the detective say to the grateful bank manager?

_____

Signposts

WHAT PROBLEMS DO CITIES FACE?

During the last hundred years, the United States has become a nation of city people. About 70 percent of its citizens now live in or near a city. The main reason for the growth of cities is not hard to find: People tend to live where they can find jobs. Most cities also offer good schools and stores. They are centers for health care, entertainment, and sports. It is easy for almost anyone to find friends in a city.

Yet cities also have their problems. If you live in a city, you know them well.

Crowds. Many Americans say they would rather not live in a city because of the crowding. In the central cities, large numbers of people live in a small area. And even with the crowds, some people can feel lonely because they are surrounded by strangers.

Pollution. Waste from factories and homes threatens the life of many large cities. Getting good drinking water is often a problem. A number of cities suffer from *smog* (a smoky fog). Tons of *pollutants* rise into the air from the burning of coal, gasoline, and oil. Smog not only makes everything dirty. It also attacks the eyes, throat, and lungs.

Some kinds of smog turn into acid that eats away at stone, concrete, and metal.

Noise. Some experts think that the noise level in some cities is a health hazard. Noise can be a special problem near airports. At one time, airports were built several miles from the cities. But by now, many cities have grown to surround their airports.

Crime. People in large cities usually name crime as their greatest problem. The rate of crime in cities is three times that of country areas. The *crime rate* (number of serious crimes per 100,000 people) is highest in the poorer sections of cities. Unlike the many poor people who live in the country, the *urban* poor are crowded together. Crimes like mugging and murder are usually committed by poor people against other poor people.

Flight to the suburbs. Millions of Americans have tried to escape the problems of the cities. For many, this has meant moving to the *suburbs*, the smaller towns around the big cities. This in itself has created another big problem for our cities. Today, in fact, more people live in suburbs than in cities.

AIR QUALITY IN SELECTED CITIES—1980[1]

City	Number of Days			
	good or moderate	unhealthful	very unhealthful	hazardous
Los Angeles, CA	145	109	110	2
New York, NY	235	129	2	0
Houston, TX	265	80	21	0
Denver, CO	277	62	23	4
Philadelphia, PA	303	59	4	0
Chicago, IL	318	45	3	0
Kansas City, MO	329	36	1	0
Seattle, WA	333	33	0	0

[1]SOURCE: *Statistical Abstract of the United States 1982–83*, U.S. Department of Commerce, Bureau of the Census.

Why do you think the largest cities usually have the greatest problem with air pollution?

644

► Can you always understand what you read? Can you always remember what you want to? This is not easy. It is especially difficult when you read a textbook.

There are several ways of reading that can help you. Skimming is one of the most important. You should skim to see what is ahead before you read with care. At the start of your reading, notice certain features. They are like signposts telling you in which direction to go. Look for the following features when you skim textbook pages:

- A title or main heading
- Any questions that follow the title or heading
- Any pictures, as well as words over or under them
- The subheads (smaller headings of separate paragraphs or parts)
- Any words in **heavy black type** and their meanings
- Any words in *italics* and their meanings
- The first sentence of each paragraph (Skim these quickly.)
- Any charts, graphs, or maps, as well as words over or under them
- Any questions at the end of the reading ■

SKILL BUILDER 28

Directions: First, skim sample page 644 (opposite). Look for the features listed above. Then try to complete the following sentences without looking back.

1. The main topic that begins on the page is _____

2. The first subtopic found on the page is _____

3. The first sentence of paragraph one tells you that _____

4. The word *pollutants* means _____

5. The word *urban* means _____

6. The *crime rate* is defined as _____

7. City people usually say their greatest problem is _____

8. The noise level in some cities may be _____

9. The chart gives information about the problem of _____

10. In 1980, how many cities had more than 50 days of poor air quality? _____

Skim Before You Read Carefully

THE ALCHEMIST'S DREAM COME TRUE

◎ **TARGET—How are some elements changed into new elements?**

Do you remember the story of King Midas? Everything he touched changed to gold. Of course, this story is not true. For hundreds of years, though, people have been trying to change one element into another. The first attempts were made by people called **alchemists** (AL-kem-ists). The alchemists were the first chemists. Many of them believed that they would be able to change cheap lead into gold. They did many experiments. Their work went on for years, but no one ever found a way to turn lead into gold.

RADIUM AND RADON

Chemists today do not spend their time trying to make gold out of cheap metals. But they can change some elements into others. And there are some elements that change naturally. **Radium** (RAY-dee-um), for example, changes into the element **radon** (RAY-don). Little by little, the radium gives off rays. When a radium atom breaks up, it loses 2 *protons*, 2 *electrons*, and 2 *neutrons*. What is left is a new element, radon.

What happens to the 2 protons, 2 electrons, and 2 neutrons that are given off? They form a **helium** (HEE-lee-um) atom. Helium is a very light gas. You may have once watched a *helium balloon* rise into the clouds!

NEW ELEMENTS ARE MADE BY MACHINES

New elements can be made by adding protons to an atom or by splitting the atom. How is this done? Scientists today have a wonderful new tool called a **cyclotron** (SY-klo-tron). It is a sort of racetrack for protons. The protons move around the inside of the cyclotron faster and faster. Then they are "shot" into an element. When these protons hit an atom, one of two things may happen. The proton can enter the atom and stay there. Or the atom can split apart into atoms of other kinds. In this way new elements are formed.

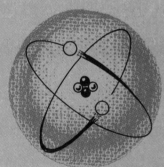

Figure 1: A helium atom

Atoms are too small to see, but it is helpful to think they look something like this. The 2 electrons whirl around the outside. The protons and neutrons are at the center. A radium atom, of course, would be much heavier: 88 protons, 88 electrons, and 138 neutrons.

174

The last lesson covered the all-important skill of beginning a reading assignment by skimming it. You should practice this skill until it becomes a habit. The reading road is always smoother when you know where you're going.

This lesson will give you more practice in skimming before reading. It will add another important skill—*asking yourself questions*. A good reader attacks a reading assignment this way:

- Skim for signposts.
- Ask yourself questions.
- Read with care.
- Answer questions—both those in the book and those you thought of yourself. ▪

SKILL BUILDER 29

Directions: Turn back to page 39 and review the signposts to look for when you skim. Then look at sample page 174 (opposite). Skim it for signposts. Do this now before going on.

You should have spotted at least five *key words* on page 174. Try to write these five words on the lines provided *without looking back*. An example is given you.

*   *alchemists*   2. _____   4. _____

1. _____   3. _____   5. _____

SKILL BUILDER 30

Directions: Before you read page 174 carefully, ask yourself some questions about it. Make sure your questions are about main points you need to learn more about. Add four questions to the list below. Try to fit each of your questions on one line.

1. *Who was King Midas?*   (if you have forgotten)

2. _____

3. _____

4. _____

5. _____

Now go back and read page 174 with care. Be sure that you can answer all five questions above.

Go on to the next page. →

HOW IT ALL BEGAN

Today scientists use cyclotrons to learn more about the nature of matter. Doctors and dentists make use of X rays. Many people use electricity that comes from atomic power. Our understanding of the atom permits us to do many things. But how did it all begin?

HENRI BECQUEREL

In 1896 the French scientist Becquerel (bek-REL) was doing experiments with crystals containing **uranium** (you-RAY-nee-um), a rare and very heavy metal. He thought the crystals might give off X rays when placed under bright sunlight. He wrapped some photographic film in black cloth. Over the cloth he put a sheet of aluminum. On the aluminum he scattered the crystals. His experiment was all set to go, but for one thing—the day was cloudy and dull.

That was a Thursday. Becquerel put his experiment in a drawer to wait for better weather. But Friday, also, was dull. So was Saturday. When the sun failed to shine on Sunday, Becquerel—and to this day, no one knows quite why—decided to develop the film anyhow. He was amazed to discover that the crystals had caused an image to appear on the film. This had happened without light and through a sheet of metal!

MARIE AND PIERRE CURIE

It was not until several years later that Becquerel fully understood the importance of his discovery. Meanwhile, another scientist, Marie Curie, went on with the work. She thought that the rays given off by uranium might have something to do with changes in the atoms themselves. Working with her husband Pierre, she proved that this was true. The atom was not solid after all. It was breaking apart! Marie Curie gave the name *radioactivity* to the new discovery.

Marie Curie

PROFILE OF A SCIENTIST: MARIE SKLODOWSKA CURIE

Marie Sklodowska was born in Warsaw, Poland, in 1867. Her father was a science teacher. She was an excellent student. Much to her father's delight, her first love was science. In 1891 she went to Paris, France, to study physics.

Soon Marie had two loves: her new love was Pierre Curie, her professor. Before long they were married. They became the Mr.-and-Mrs. team of the scientific world. Their special interest was radioactivity. First they worked with uranium. Then they discovered that there were other heavy metals that were even more radioactive than uranium. They discovered two new elements, *radium* and *polonium*. For this work, Marie and Pierre Curie and Henri Becquerel received the Nobel Prize. Marie Curie was the first and only woman to receive the Nobel Prize in physics.

In 1906 Pierre Curie was killed by a horse-drawn carriage as he was crossing a Paris street. Marie took over his job as a professor. She went on with her experiments. In 1911 she received the Nobel Prize a second time— for producing radium in its pure form. She was the first person in history to be awarded a second Nobel Prize.

175

▶ Since the page opposite continues the science reading, there is no chapter heading. Neither are there questions aimed at the reader. For this page, skimming means looking for the following signposts:

- Any pictures
- The subheads
- Any words in **heavy black type** and their meanings
- Any words in *italics* and their meanings
- The first sentence of each paragraph ▪

SKILL BUILDER 31

Directions: Skim sample page 175 (opposite). This should take only a few seconds. Then answer the following questions on the lines.

1. What is the general topic covered on this page?

_____

2. Who are the three important people discussed on the page?

a. _____

b. _____

c. _____

3. What are four key words printed in either **heavy black type** or *italics*?

a. _____

b. _____

c. _____

d. _____

4. Which person is specially featured on this page?

_____

5. What is one important thing this person did?

_____

Putting It All Together

▶ Here is a page from another textbook. Suppose that it is the first page of a reading assignment for another class. Your homework is to read and understand the material. Of course, you want to do this in as short a time as possible. In other words, your purpose is to read with speed and accuracy.

How would you attack the assignment? The Skill Builder on the next page will help you review the best methods of reading. ▪

280

Learning About Insurance
TARGET QUESTIONS:

What is insurance?   How does it help us?

The word *insurance* means protection. We know that there are many kinds of insurance. There is fire insurance. There is life insurance. There is health insurance. But many of us don't really know what insurance is. We don't know how it works. It is best explained through fire insurance.

Let's say that you lived in a small city. Most of the houses are worth about $30,000 each. Then let's suppose that your house burned down. You would have lost all the money that you paid for the house. There would be no way of getting back any part of the money.

You would not be the only worried person. Other people would worry about their own houses. A group of people might meet to discuss the problem. Sooner or later, they would find the answer. Each house owner could put up a certain amount of money every year. The total collected would be placed in a fund. Then the fund would pay for future fire losses.

SKILL BUILDER 32

Directions: Review what you have learned about reading by circling the letter of each correct choice.

1. The exact title of the lesson, "Learning About Insurance," would also be found
   (A) in the index.
   (B) in the table of contents.
   (C) at the end of the chapter.
   (D) (all of the above)

2. If you want to know if the book has more facts about insurance, you should first skim
   (A) the top of every page.
   (B) the table of contents.
   (C) the index.
   (D) all charts and pictures.

3. Your fingers could be a real help in finding information
   (A) on page 280.
   (B) in the table of contents.
   (C) in the book's index.
   (D) nowhere, because fingers should never be seen when reading!

4. Skimming the first sentence of each paragraph tells you that
   (A) an example is given on the page.
   (B) the "target questions" have no answers.
   (C) the chapter will go on for many more pages.
   (D) (none of the above)

5. *Italic* type is used for the word "insurance." This tells you that the word
   (A) should be written down immediately.
   (B) is sure to appear on a test.
   (C) should be looked up in a dictionary.
   (D) is a key word in the chapter.

6. The two "target questions"
   (A) should be skipped over at first.
   (B) would be much more helpful at the end of the selection.
   (C) are given to guide you to the important facts in the selection.
   (D) should be printed in a different order.

7. Unlike many textbooks, this one does not seem to contain
   (A) subheads in special type.
   (B) chapter titles.
   (C) questions to help the reader.
   (D) numbered pages.

8. In skimming the page for signposts, it would be good to glance at
   (A) all words more than half an inch long.
   (B) all words starting with capital letters.
   (C) certain words in the index.
   (D) the first sentence of every paragraph.

9. Right after skimming for signposts, it would be a good idea to
   (A) make an outline before you read.
   (B) ask yourself some questions.
   (C) read the page aloud.
   (D) answer the "target questions" in detail.

10. The last step in reading a school assignment should be
    (A) looking for key words.
    (B) memorizing topic sentences.
    (C) checking your understanding by answering questions.
    (D) copying it into your notebook.

SKILL BUILDER 33

Directions: Now write two good questions about textbook page 280. You can start by copying one of the "target questions" if you think it is more important than your own.

1. _____

2. _____

Go on to the next page. →

Suppose that thirty people got together. They might put up $1,000 each. This would pay for the average house if it burned down. But $1,000 is a lot of money. Besides, it isn't likely that one house in thirty will burn. It would be better for more people to join the fund. Suppose 300 people joined. Then each one would have to pay only $100. Better still, suppose 3,000 people joined. Then each share would cost only $10.

Such a fund could be called a protection fund, or *insurance* fund. Every house owner would put some money into it every year. The actual payments, of course, would depend on the value of the house. People with costly homes would pay more. These yearly payments are now called *premiums*. They are figured at a certain amount for each $1,000 worth of protection. For example, suppose the premium rate, or cost, were $5 for each $1,000 of insurance. The premium for a $30,000 house would be 30 x $5, or $150.

282

All kinds of insurance work the same way. People join together to spread the risk. Life insurance spreads the risk of dying. It's as though many people put money into a pot. Then, if one of them dies, the money goes to that person's family. In the same way, health insurance spreads the risk of getting sick. It pays for large doctor and hospital bills. Many people, of course, pay premiums for years and never collect any money. Yet they are glad to pay because they know what *might* happen. Thus insurance is really protection.

SKILL BUILDER 34

Directions: The selection on insurance continues on the opposite page. First, skim the rest of the lesson for signposts. Then think of two more good questions. Write them on the numbered lines below.

1. _____

2. _____

Now go back and read the whole selection with care. When you finish reading, write out the answers to your questions.

SKILL BUILDER 35

Directions: Complete the following exercise. Try not to look back.

1. What is a premium? _____

2. Very few people really expect their homes to burn. Yet most people buy insurance because

   _____

3. Why might one house owner buy more insurance than another? _____

   _____

4. The rate of fire insurance means the amount paid per year for every $1,000 of insurance. True or false? (Circle the correct answer.)

5. If the rate of insurance is $6, what is the premium for a $50,000 house? _____

6. The picture on page 281 is supposed to suggest that (A) insured houses do not burn (B) the house on the left is protected by insurance (C) insurance costs too much money.

7. Life insurance (A) costs less than fire insurance (B) helps many people live longer (C) spreads the risk of dying.

8. People with a lot of health insurance (A) probably feel easier in mind than those with little or none (B) can forget about the rules of good health (C) certainly see doctors more often.

9. People who pay premiums but never collect money (A) should feel cheated (B) certainly did not need the insurance (C) should feel thankful.

10. The answer to this question is not in the selection. But if you think for a moment, you should be able to get it. It is a fact that life insurance rates for women are lower than those for men. Why might this be so?

   _____

   _____

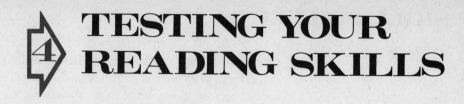

TESTING YOUR READING SKILLS

Questions, Please

▶ As this book has made clear, people read for many different purposes. Sometimes your purpose is to do your best on a test. When that is the case—*watch out!* Even if you know the material very well, something about the test questions can throw you off stride and leave you limping toward wrong answers.

The people who make up tests can seem to be devilish sorts. Just when you think you've seen every kind of question, they make up a new one that confuses you. Look, for instance, at the first test item below. It is very much like one given not long ago to every grade-nine student in a certain state. Some students found it a puzzle.

Here's a useful rule to remember: When you come to a test item of a kind you haven't seen before, first *skim* it to discover (1) how it is organized, and (2) exactly what you are supposed to do. Don't just start reading with the very first line. You might just be wasting your time. ▪

SKILL BUILDER 36

Directions: Skim each test item to discover what you are supposed to do. Then do it!

A. Prunes are hardly America's favorite food. In fact, among certain groups, prunes are something of a joke. The California prune Board tries hard to make prunes more popular.² They give away many free samples. They point out that a prune is really nothing but a dried³ plum—and "plum" is a word people seem to like. Yet so far, the drive⁴ to make "black diamonds" more populer⁵ hasn't met with much success.

1. Circle the number of the word that is misspelled.

  1   2   3   4   5

2. Write the underlined word that contains an error. Correct it at the same time.

B. Carl is younger than Marge. Marge is younger than her sister. Cris is older than Marge.

Underline any statement(s) that must be true.
(a) Cris and Marge are sisters.
(b) Marge's sister is older than Cris.
(c) Cris is older than Carl.
(d) Cris must be a boy.

C. Look at the paragraph topic given below. Study the five details that the paragraph might contain. Four of the details should be used in the paragraph. Write the letter of the detail that should *not* be used on the line to the left of the numeral.

_____ 1. Topic: Costs of modern schools
  (a) teachers' pay

(b) painting and repairs
(c) test scores of small-town pupils
(d) gallons of fuel oil per pupil
(e) books and paper

======

D. In the space provided at the left, write the correct form of the word in parentheses (--).

_____ Juanita is (happy) on Saturdays than on Sundays.

======

E. The following sentence contains an error: "Is an *autobiography* life story of a car?"

The sentence would be correct if the writer had added the word (circle):

for   than   the

be   its   an

======

F. The paragraph below contains four numbered blanks. Write in each blank the word that seems to make the most sense. Choose your words from the lists that follow the passage.

A mnemonic (nee MON ik) device is a little _(1)_____ that helps you remember something. Look, for instance, at the first two _(2)_____ of that odd word *mnemonic*. Which comes first in the alphabet, the *m* or the *n*? One student remembered that the *m* was the "big, broad-shouldered one." Like a football player, it "plowed through the line," making way for its _(3)_____ friend *n* that followed. Other students have remem-

bered that the first three letters of *piece* are *pie*: a *piece of pie*. The word *separate* has *a rat* in it. The word *parallel* has two _(4)_____ lines in the middle. *Accommodate* can "accommodate" both two *c*'s and two *m*'s.

1. dishonesty, fooler, machine, trick, strange
2. letters, syllables, sounds, rhymes, vowels
3. fat, slower, new-found, false, slender
4. odd, curving, parallel, imaginary, incorrect

======

G. Roberto reads lots of books by modern authors, M. E. Kerr, I think, is his favorite. He suggested that I read *The Son of Someone Famous*. However, I haven't yet been able to find the book.

There is one mistake in the short paragraph above. It involves (circle):

spelling

punctuation

capitals

underlining or italics

Test-taking Tips

In this book, you've learned how to skim to find the exact information you need. You've also practiced reading with greater speed and understanding by seeing words in groups. These skills can help you during tests. Remember the following tips.

- Often you will see a paragraph followed by questions. Sometimes it's a good idea to start by skimming the first question or two. Try picking out some key words to look for. Then skim the paragraph. Finally, read carefully to answer the questions.
- See words in groups. Take in *who, what, when, where,* and *why* words at a glance. Keeping up your reading speed will enable you to finish the test in the time allowed.

As you work on the test that follows, you'll read about other test-taking tips. Use them! ■

SKILL BUILDER 37

Directions: This book ends with five reading tests. Do your best on them. For the test below, circle the letters of the correct answers in the box on page 51.

". . . Are there any final questions? No? All right, open your test booklets and begin work."

Paper rattles as 30 booklets open at once. One nervous student drops a pencil. Others laugh. Then suddenly all is serious. Thirty pairs of eyes begin reading.

Michelle and Carmen are in the back row. They are equally good readers. But today Carmen will get a much higher mark in reading. Why? She's ready for the test—rested, alert, and calm. Michelle, on the other hand, is not ready. She yawned her way through "The Late Show" the night before. She woke up grumpy. She skipped breakfast. Just before the test, she had gym. A hard game of basketball left her tired. And even worse, an argument in gym left her steaming.

1. Which statement best expresses the main idea of the passage?
   (A) Nervous people laugh easily.
   (B) Hungry people don't usually do their best on tests.
   (C) Carmen is a bad girl.
   (D) How a student gets ready for a test affects his or her marks.

2. The passage starts with the voice of
   (A) a testing machine.
   (B) the teacher.
   (C) a girl.
   (D) the principal.
3. Michelle and Carmen were sitting
   (A) next to the windows.
   (B) next to each other.
   (C) in the front.
   (D) in the back.
4. The word *steaming* (last word) here means
   (A) angry and upset.
   (B) damp or wet.
   (C) very hot.
   (D) breathing into the cold air.

Clearly, equally good readers do not always get the same marks on tests. Some are more ready than others. Some also know more about tests. They recognize certain kinds of questions when they come to them.

Reading tests include several kinds of questions. But four kinds are used over and over. Look at question 1 on this page. It is a "main idea" question. It asks you what the *whole* passage is about. ("Central thought" or "best title" questions do the same thing.) Question 2 is an "inference" question. It asks for something not directly stated in the passage. Question 3 is a "fact" question. It asks for a detail. Just make sure to pick the *one* answer that you're *sure* is right. And question 4 is a "context" question. You are asked to get the meaning of a word from its sentence.

5. The term that does not belong with the others is
   (A) main idea.
   (B) central thought.
   (C) inference.
   (D) best title.
6. An inference (idea not stated) from the passage you just read is that
   (A) many poor test takers fail to spot and know four kinds of questions when they see them.
   (B) context questions are usually the hardest of all.
   (C) some students know more about tests than others.
   (D) relaxed students have a better chance than tense students.
7. Most alike are
   (A) inference and fact questions.
   (B) fact and best title questions.
   (C) context and fact questions.
   (D) inference and context questions.

=====

There! That last question was a wowzer. How much time did you spend on it? Spending too much time on single questions is a bad habit. Give hard questions a fair amount of time, but *get on with the test*. Your job is not to answer the ten hardest questions on the test. It is to get as many items right as possible.

Clock watching is another bad habit. Sure, it's all right to glance at the clock once in a while. It's even okay to figure where you should be when the time is half over. But many students forget about the clock and do just fine. Work as fast and ac-

curately as you can. Keep going.

Other poor test takers keep losing their place. *Use your hands*. Keep one finger by the question you're answering. Keep another, and your pencil, over the right place on the answer sheet.

Still another bad habit is trying for a pretty answer sheet. The correcting machine doesn't know what "pretty" means. Your pencil can do the job in a second. Those little circles and spaces don't have to be *completely* filled in. Too much neatness here gets you nowhere.

And finally, "don't guess" means don't guess *blindly*. Sometimes you have a feeling that a certain answer is right. Maybe you can't begin to explain the reason for your hunch. But that doesn't matter. Go ahead and put it down.

8. Which statement does the passage support?
   (A) Be 100% sure of each answer.
   (B) Finish the entire answer sheet.
   (C) Follow your hunches.
   (D) Hard questions count for more.
9. The author says that students should
   (A) mark up the test booklet.
   (B) look at the clock.
   (C) work fast and accurately.
   (D) guess wildly.
10. As used here, the word *pretty* means
    (A) very neat and tidy.
    (B) reasonable.
    (C) moving.
    (D) exciting.

PUT ALL ANSWERS HERE

1. A B C D
2. A B C D
3. A B C D
4. A B C D
5. A B C D
6. A B C D
7. A B C D
8. A B C D
9. A B C D
10. A B C D

READING TEST 1

Directions: Read each passage and answer the questions. Make an **X** in the right box.

It was a boring summer. I hung around the house a lot. I used to get up late and watch TV. It would drive Mom crazy. Sooner or later she'd order me to go outside. Down at Maxwell's, I'd meet some of the kids. They were as bored as I was. Sometimes Max would give us little two-bit jobs. We'd wash a car or load a truck with old tires. All the money went into the soft-drink machine. I drank two or three cans a day.

1. The person said to be driven "crazy" is
   (A) the writer
   (B) Max
   (C) Mom
   (D) one of the kids

   A B C D
   1. ☐ ☐ ☐ ☐

2. You can figure out that Maxwell's is a
   (A) TV store
   (B) candy store
   (C) supermarket
   (D) garage

   A B C D
   2. ☐ ☐ ☐ ☐

3. The writer can best be described as not having
   (A) ambition and energy
   (B) any friends
   (C) strength and health
   (D) food and clothing

   A B C D
   3. ☐ ☐ ☐ ☐

4. Money earned by the writer was spent for
   (A) tires
   (B) soft drinks
   (C) candy
   (D) pay TV

   A B C D
   4. ☐ ☐ ☐ ☐

═══════════════

The strange building stood beside Route 44 for over forty years. It was in the shape of a giant milk bottle. No one could miss seeing it. It was forty feet (12 m) high. It measured fifty-eight feet (18 m) around. "Look at *that!*" tourists would say. Many of them would stop for a milkshake or a hot dog. Slowly the wooden building got old. Its shape grew more and more old-fashioned. The white paint peeled. In 1976 a milk company gave $80,000 to fix up the huge bottle. It was moved from Taunton, Massachusetts, to Boston. Now it's a museum piece. Tourists will say "Look at *that!*" for many more years.

5. Before 1976 the huge milk bottle stood
   (A) near Route 40
   (B) near Route 44
   (C) near Route 58
   (D) in Boston

   A B C D
   5. ☐ ☐ ☐ ☐

6. You can figure out that the building was once a
   (A) milk-storage plant
   (B) barn
   (C) roadside garage
   (D) fast-food restaurant

   A B C D
   6. ☐ ☐ ☐ ☐

7. Money to repair and move the building was given by
   (A) cow farmers
   (B) a milk company
   (C) the state government
   (D) its former owners

   A B C D
   7. ☐ ☐ ☐ ☐

8. We can tell from the selection that Route 44 passes
   (A) through Boston
   (B) by many odd buildings
   (C) through Taunton
   (D) across Massachusetts

   A B C D
   8. ☐ ☐ ☐ ☐

9. As used here, the term *museum piece* means something
   (A) inside a museum building
   (B) old and interesting
   (C) concerning food
   (D) made of wood

   A B C D
   9. ☐ ☐ ☐ ☐

═══════════════

How big are the biggest hailstones? No one knows for sure. Hailstones that weighed hundreds of pounds have been reported. The stories are heard in all kinds of places from New Mexico to New Hampshire. But we have no proof for most of them.

A Pennsylvania farmer once told an odd story. He said a huge hailstone had fallen near him in a field. It cracked upon landing. The ground was covered with pieces of ice. He put some of the ice in a freezer. Scientists saw it, but they never saw the hailstone itself.

Every summer newspapers carry stories of huge hailstones. They are said to be as large as golf balls—some news stories say "baseballs" or even "softballs." The trouble is that they melt quickly. We do have proof of a huge hailstone that fell at Potter, Nebraska, on July 6, 1928. It was weighed and measured. Photos were taken. It weighed a pound and a half (43 g). It was five inches (13 cm) across.

The Nebraska hailstone was a little bigger than a softball. It seems likely that even larger ones have fallen. Hailstones can go through roofs of houses. They can also penetrate car tops and hoods.

10. The selection is chiefly about the
(A) danger of hailstones
(B) cause of hailstones
(C) size of hailstones
(D) pictures of hailstones
10. □ □ □ □
    A B C D

11. The largest hailstone *on record* fell in
(A) New Mexico
(B) New Hampshire
(C) Pennsylvania
(D) Nebraska
11. □ □ □ □
    A B C D

12. The largest hailstones *on record* are about the size of
(A) golf balls
(B) baseballs
(C) softballs
(D) basketballs
12. □ □ □ □
    A B C D

13. The word *penetrate* (last line) means
(A) fall on
(B) paint
(C) go through
(D) scratch
13. □ □ □ □
    A B C D

14. It is hard to check on hailstones because they
(A) crack easily
(B) make poor pictures
(C) are oddly shaped
(D) melt
14. □ □ □ □
    A B C D

═══════════════

People who run for office sometimes make odd claims. One of these claims is this:

"If elected, I'm going to go in there and clean the Augean [aw JEE un] stables."

What does this mean? What are (or were) the "Augean stables"?

A stable, of course, is a barn. The Augean stables were those of Augeas. He was a king in ancient Greece. He was supposed to have owned 3,000 sacred oxen. Their stables had not been cleaned in thirty years. Then along came Hercules, the strong man of myth. Hercules agreed to clean the stables in a single day. He harnessed two rivers. He turned them through the stables. The barns were swept clean. Later, Augeas refused to pay Hercules. In anger, Hercules sent an army to the kingdom. Augeas and his sons were killed.

Thus, a politician who speaks of "Augean stables" means three things: 1) the party in power has made a real mess of things; 2) cleaning up the mess is a task almost beyond human power; 3) I have great ability like Hercules.

15. Two time periods are discussed in the selection. The first is modern America. The second is
(A) early America
(B) ancient Greece
(C) modern Greece
(D) old England
15. □ □ □ □
    A B C D

16. The stables of King Augeas held
(A) goats and sheep
(B) horses
(C) grain for ten years
(D) oxen
16. □ □ □ □
    A B C D

17. Hercules cleaned the Augean stables with the help of
(A) an army
(B) a broom
(C) two rivers
(D) a harness
17. □ □ □ □
    A B C D

18. Today "Augean stables" is commonly used to mean
(A) City Hall
(B) Waterfront Stadium
(C) any dirty barn
(D) large banks
18. □ □ □ □
    A B C D

19. The best title for the selection is
(A) Modern Politics
(B) Hercules
(C) The Augean Stables
(D) King Augeas
19. □ □ □ □
    A B C D

═══════════════

Cousins are confusing. First cousins have one set of grandparents in common. Second cousins have in common one set of great-grandparents. The child of your first cousin is your first cousin *once removed*. (He or she is *not* your "second cousin," as is sometimes said.) Also, of course, your parents' first cousins are your first cousins once removed.

20. Certain key words in the paragraph above tell the good reader at once that it deals with
(A) friendships
(B) first names
(C) relationships
(D) family conflict
20. □ □ □ □
    A B C D

READING TEST 2

Directions: Use a pencil to fill in the correct answers in the box on page 55.

Cockroaches are pests known to most city dwellers. They will eat almost anything—garbage, grease, even old shoes. They often hide in the daytime, waiting for lights to be turned off. Then they explore the damp areas around kitchen sinks. They also like to eat the covering on some electrical wires. Your refrigerator isn't working? Its motor may be clogged with roaches.

Some poisons will kill cockroaches or at least make them go away. But keep that poison handy! The roaches will be back. The ones you see next may be sons and daughters of the ones that left. If so, they may laugh at your poison. Cockroaches have been around since the time of the dinosaurs. They will probably be around for millions of more years.

1. Cockroaches are probably most common in
   (A) country areas
   (B) cities
   (C) the Southwest
   (D) new homes
2. Roaches seem to like all the following EXCEPT
   (A) darkness
   (B) dirtiness
   (C) draftiness
   (D) dampness
3. Poisons sold to kill cockroaches are
   (A) not effective
   (B) somewhat effective
   (C) completely effective
   (D) very harmful to humans
4. Roaches have lived on the earth
   (A) for millions of years
   (B) since the earth was formed
   (C) only since humans appeared
   (D) (none of the above)
5. A word in the second paragraph that doesn't really mean what it seems to say is
   (A) *roaches*
   (B) *next*
   (C) *laugh*
   (D) *dinosaurs*

———————————

Another kind of strange plant is the mushroom. Most plants are green and make their own food—but not the lowly mushroom. Mushrooms look like white or brown umbrellas with thick handles. They have no leaves, flowers, seeds, or fruits. They get their food from rotting plants in the soil. Because they need no

light, they can grow in the dark. Mushroom "farms" in France consist of miles of tunnels.

Poisonous mushrooms are often called "toadstools." (Long ago, people thought that poisonous toads sat on them.) The worst killer may be the small *amanita,* or "death angel." You can tell it by the tiny cup at the bottom of its stem. But other kinds of mushrooms are nearly as deadly. Unless you're an expert, don't go out picking mushrooms for food.

6. The paragraph that originally came just before this passage discussed
   (A) mushrooms
   (B) toadstools
   (C) common plants
   (D) odd plants
7. Like most plants, mushrooms seem to
   (A) make their own food
   (B) have roots
   (C) need sunlight
   (D) have green leaves
8. You would be most likely to find mushrooms
   (A) in the shade of an old apple tree
   (B) deep in a coal mine
   (C) in the desert
   (D) where brick buildings have recently been destroyed
9. In France, mushrooms are grown
   (A) on rooftops
   (B) underground
   (C) under grape vines
   (D) at high altitudes
10. The word *toadstool*
    (A) means exactly the same as *mushroom*
    (B) is no longer used
    (C) comes from an old superstition
    (D) has no use in the modern world
11. The "death angel"
    (A) has a winglike top
    (B) makes good eating
    (C) is not a true mushroom
    (D) has a small cup at its base
12. Which statement is correct?
    (A) Toadstools are deadly, but mushrooms are not.
    (B) All mushrooms are deadly.
    (C) Some mushrooms are deadly.
    (D) No mushrooms are deadly.

In the year 1284, an old legend tells us, the small city of Hamelin, Germany, was overrun with rats. Rats were everywhere. The people didn't know what to do.

One day a tall stranger came to town. He was
• dressed in pied clothing—red, yellow, brown, and gray. He walked into Hamelin playing tunes on a long pipe. The Pied Piper said that, for a price, he would rid Hamelin of its rats. The people laughed at the idea. But still, they thought, why not give it a try? They agreed to pay the Pied Piper a big sum—but only after the rats were gone.

Playing a happy tune on his pipe, the stranger marched through the streets. Soon the rats came running to line up behind him. Before long dozens of rats were marching behind the piper. Then there were hundreds . . . thousands . . . hundreds of thousands. The Pied Piper led his rat army into a nearby river. The rats drowned, and the stranger returned for his payment.

But the people refused to pay. Why should they? The rats were gone. What could the Pied Piper do about it?

Alas, the people were sadly mistaken. Once again the Pied Piper began to walk through the streets. This time he played a different tune. And this time it was the children who followed him. When all the children had gathered behind him, he led them toward Kuppelberg Hill. A hole opened in the side of the hill. Into it marched the Pied Piper and all the children. Then the hole closed up again, as strangely as it had opened.

The children were gone, but the Pied Piper's lesson lives on to this day: *One must always pay the piper.*

13. The passage is called a
(A) true story
(B) myth
(C) legend
(D) fable
14. The idea of Hamelin's being overrun with rats in 1284 is
(A) impossible
(B) very hard to believe
(C) easy to believe
(D) (none of the above)
15. The word *pied*—marked with a bullet (•)—means
(A) "playing a pipe"
(B) "unknown; strange"
(C) "scientific"
(D) "of different colors"
16. The whole story of the Pied Piper of Hamelin is
(A) impossible
(B) very hard to believe
(C) easy to believe
(D) (none of the above)

17. First to march behind the Pied Piper were
(A) rats
(B) adults
(C) children
(D) people carrying silver coins
18. It makes sense to think that
(A) the city of Hamelin never existed
(B) most people believed the Pied Piper when he first made his offer
(C) most people thought the large payment would never have to be made
(D) the lesson of the story is that children are like rats
19. The Pied Piper's final act shows that he was filled with
(A) admiration
(B) sorrow
(C) love of children
(D) revenge
20. Which statement best expresses the meaning of the story?
(A) Never judge a man by his appearance.
(B) Music has strange powers that most people cannot even imagine.
(C) You must always pay for services performed.
(D) Hold your laughter if it might hurt the feelings of others.

PUT ALL ANSWERS HERE

	A	B	C	D		A	B	C	D
1.	‖	‖	‖	‖	11.	‖	‖	‖	‖
2.	‖	‖	‖	‖	12.	‖	‖	‖	‖
3.	‖	‖	‖	‖	13.	‖	‖	‖	‖
4.	‖	‖	‖	‖	14.	‖	‖	‖	‖
5.	‖	‖	‖	‖	15.	‖	‖	‖	‖
6.	‖	‖	‖	‖	16.	‖	‖	‖	‖
7.	‖	‖	‖	‖	17.	‖	‖	‖	‖
8.	‖	‖	‖	‖	18.	‖	‖	‖	‖
9.	‖	‖	‖	‖	19.	‖	‖	‖	‖
10.	‖	‖	‖	‖	20.	‖	‖	‖	‖

READING TEST 3

Directions: Read the passages and answer the questions. Put all answers on the bottom of page 57.

All minorities should be treated fairly. That's what I really believe. The trouble is, I belong to a minority whose rights are ignored every day. I'm one of the millions of people who can accurately be called *short*.

Don't laugh. Have you ever thought about the daily life of a person who's only four-ten? I can't reach the top shelves in stores. I can't be a police officer or even join the army. Most people look down their noses at me. Troubles like these are bad enough, but the worst thing is that the language seems rigged against us short people.

What happens when a store clerk returns to you the wrong amount of money? You're *short*changed, of course. And is it good to be *short*-tempered or *short*sighted? Of course it isn't. Neither is it good to run *short* of money or fall *short* on the job. With so

• many *short*comings, how can I ever be both *short* and sweet?

1. The best title for the passage is
   (A) No Shortage Here
   (B) A Short Story
   (C) The Trouble with Being Short
   (D) Tall or Short?
2. The selection was most likely written by a
   (A) tall person
   (B) short person
   (C) tall woman
   (D) short man
3. The author claims to be a member of
   (A) a group of shortsighted people
   (B) the army
   (C) a minority
   (D) a self-help club
4. The word *shortcomings*—marked with a bullet (•)—means
   (A) weak points; defects
   (B) failures to arrive
   (C) times of anger
   (D) short friends
5. Another example that might have been used in the last paragraph is the term
   (A) "short wait"
   (B) "shortstop"
   (C) "shortening"
   (D) "short-winded"

Do people take soap operas for real? Strange as it seems, many people do. Dr. Marlena Evans was a character on NBC's "Days of Our Lives." As soon as the character was murdered, the phones started to ring. Soon Deidre Hall, the actress who played the part, was asked to take the calls. NBC thought that her voice would make the people who called stop crying. She talked to more than a thousand fans. The calls went on for three days. Finally NBC decided that enough was enough. They shut down the switchboard.

6. The passage refers to
   (A) a murder in New York
   (B) an angry actress
   (C) a make-believe murder
   (D) (all of the above)
7. The author of the passage seems
   (A) to admire the people who called
   (B) to know little about soap operas
   (C) to be out for laughs
   (D) surprised at what is described
8. Dr. Marlena Evans
   (A) answered over a thousand calls
   (B) wrote the selection herself
   (C) was a character on a soap opera
   (D) acted in "Days of Our Lives"
9. The "phones" mentioned probably were
   (A) in NBC headquarters
   (B) in Deidre Hall's apartment
   (C) those of Dr. Evans
   (D) not answered at first
10. According to the passage, the callers were
   (A) nearly all women
   (B) half teenagers
   (C) angry at Deidre Hall
   (D) crying, at least at times

EVERY DAY OF YOUR LIFE—
1. You inhale 440 cubic feet (13 m³) of air.
2. You breathe 23,175 times.
3. Your heart beats 104,280 times.
4. Your blood travels 172,000 miles (276,807 km).
5. You move 753 muscles.
6. You use 8,000,000 brain cells.
7. You speak 6,200 words.

11. The word "day" in the first line probably means
   (A) the hours you're awake
   (B) 24-hour period
   (C) 12-hour period
   (D) something clever about a soap opera

12. The item that differs most from person to person is probably
(A) item 1
(B) item 3
(C) item 6
(D) item 7

13. The writer of the selection seems least sure of the number of
(A) breaths
(B) heartbeats
(C) muscles
(D) brain cells

14. The "you" referred to is imagined as being
(A) unusually active
(B) the average person
(C) highly intelligent
(D) a scientist

———————

Beware of all get-rich-quick schemes. In most of them, you'll lose money. You'll also lose time. The only person who is likely to get rich is the person who interested you in the scheme in the first place.

You see an ad in the paper: "Earn $15–20,000 a year. Part time. Small investment required." You're curious. You write to a nearby city for information. It comes in the mail. Lucky you! You're one of a few people in your state who will have rights to a certain vending-machine business. For $3,500 you can buy ten coin machines that distribute toothbrushes, razor blades, perfumes, etc. All you have to do is put them in gas-station rest rooms and collect the coins.

You fall for the scheme, borrowing most of the money. In a few days the machines arrive. You have little trouble getting permission from gas-station owners. At the end of your first week, you open the coin boxes and learn the sad truth: The machines make a lot less money than you had expected.

You phone the person who sold you the machines. There's no answer. The next day the phone is taken out. You write this •promoter, but the letter comes back stamped "MOVED. FORWARDING ADDRESS UNKNOWN." By now he or she is in another state. It's safe to guess that ads will soon appear in local papers there for a new group of the easily fooled.

15. The advice given here is probably
(A) not based on fact
(B) based on the writer's own experience
(C) not meant seriously
(D) very good indeed

16. The word *promoter*—marked with a bullet (•)—here carries the meaning
(A) shady businessperson
(B) one who promotes others
(C) beloved rascal
(D) insane person

17. The person who fell for the scheme bought ten machines that distribute
(A) maps and driving aids
(B) containers of milk and juice
(C) sandwiches
(D) toothbrushes, razor blades, etc.

18. The author of the selection does all of the following EXCEPT
(A) give an example
(B) state his main idea directly
(C) ask the reader several questions
(D) use a quotation

19. The "you" referred to is imagined as being
(A) a most clever person
(B) very suspicious throughout
(C) unable to read
(D) far from rich

20. The selection shows how some get-rich-quick schemes depend on
(A) a lack of law enforcement officers
(B) the desire of people to better themselves
(C) people's fears regarding their health
(D) good products that outsell poor ones

PUT ALL ANSWERS HERE

	A	B	C	D		A	B	C	D
1.	‖	‖	‖	‖	11.	‖	‖	‖	‖
2.	‖	‖	‖	‖	12.	‖	‖	‖	‖
3.	‖	‖	‖	‖	13.	‖	‖	‖	‖
4.	‖	‖	‖	‖	14.	‖	‖	‖	‖
5.	‖	‖	‖	‖	15.	‖	‖	‖	‖
6.	‖	‖	‖	‖	16.	‖	‖	‖	‖
7.	‖	‖	‖	‖	17.	‖	‖	‖	‖
8.	‖	‖	‖	‖	18.	‖	‖	‖	‖
9.	‖	‖	‖	‖	19.	‖	‖	‖	‖
10.	‖	‖	‖	‖	20.	‖	‖	‖	‖

READING TEST 4

Directions: Use a pencil to fill in the right circle in the box on page 59.

Spiders are not insects. In fact, they are not even closely related to insects. Spiders are related to scorpions, mites, and tics.

Spiders are unlike insects in several ways. They have eight legs. Insects have six. Spiders have two body sections. Insects have three body sections. Also, spiders have no feelers, or antennae. All insects have feelers. And spiders, of course, can spin webs.

1. You can tell the difference between spiders and insects because they are different in
   (1) size
   (2) length of life
   (3) physical make-up
   (4) color
2. One difference between spiders and insects is that spiders have no
   (1) legs
   (2) jaws
   (3) eyes
   (4) feelers
3. If you found a small, six-legged creature, it would probably be
   (1) an insect
   (2) a mite
   (3) a tic
   (4) a spider
4. The selection suggests, but does not state, that
   (1) insects never eat spiders
   (2) spiders have two body sections
   (3) feelers have no real use
   (4) insects cannot spin webs
5. The best title for the selection is
   (1) Spiders
   (2) Insects
   (3) What's the Difference?
   (4) Are Spiders Insects?

———————————

Most garages are honest. But a few are not. Be careful when driving out of state or on big highways. All drivers should know the tricks:

"Your oil filter's too hot. It should be replaced." If you hear that one, forget it. The "hot oil filter" is a $5.00 joke.

"Your right rear tire is low. It would be a good idea to put in a tube." You look at the tire, and it *is* low. But there's something you don't know. The attendant let the air out while filling your tank.

"That battery's boiling over. You need a new one." Of course the battery's boiling. It's just been treated with Alka-Seltzer!

6. Alka-Seltzer is mentioned in the passage in connection with
   (1) headaches caused by driving
   (2) oil
   (3) batteries
   (4) slipping fan belts
7. The only price mentioned is for
   (1) a hose
   (2) a tube
   (3) oil
   (4) an oil filter
8. The purpose of the passage is to show that
   (1) driving is not safe
   (2) cars are poorly made
   (3) some garages are dishonest
   (4) you should do your own car repairs
9. The author suggests that garages are more likely to cheat
   (1) teenagers
   (2) senior citizens
   (3) people from out of state
   (4) people with big cars

———————————

There are lots of books on careers for young people. But hundreds of careers are seldom mentioned. These are odd kinds of jobs that few people do.

One is whitewashing. Whitewash is a white lime spray. It is much cheaper than paint. Barns are often whitewashed. So, sometimes, are garages, and even homes. You can carry what you need easily in a car. To start you'll need a mixing tank, some pails, a sprayer, and a mask. The sprayer can be gas or electric. When you buy it, try to get an air attachment so you can blow off dust and cobwebs. The lime whitewash can be bought at most farm-supply stores. Just follow directions.

Business may be slow at first. But do a good job and you'll be called back. Charge about $60 a day, including travel time.

10. Many careers are not mentioned in books because they are
    (1) too dangerous
    (2) too expensive to start
    (3) already taught in school
    (4) practiced by few people
11. The "air attachment" in paragraph two fits on
    (1) the car used to carry equipment
    (2) the mixing tank
    (3) the sprayer
    (4) the mask
12. In order to start a whitewashing business it is necessary to have
    (1) a high-school education
    (2) experience in painting
    (3) a partner to mix paints
    (4) a car or truck
13. A whitewasher who works a full five-day week should earn about
    (1) $25 a day
    (2) $300 a week
    (3) $500 a month
    (4) $30,000 a year
14. The author's purpose in writing was to
    (1) make the reader laugh
    (2) anger the reader
    (3) provide information
    (4) (none of the above)

But the greatest fighter for women's rights may have been Lucy Stone. She was born in rural Massachusetts in 1818. She was a good student. In 1847 she was graduated from Oberlin College in Ohio. (Oberlin was one of the first colleges to give degrees to both men and women.) That year, too, she gave her first speech on women's rights. A powerful speaker, she soon gained fame across the country. People who came to laugh stayed to listen, and left persuaded. In 1850, when she married, she insisted on keeping her own name. Her wedding service, which she wrote herself, was a protest against unfair laws. At that time, husbands "owned" their wives during marriage. The wife could not own or inherit property, make a will, or sue in a court of law. She could neither keep her own earnings nor get custody of her own children.

For about ten years, antislavery work took much of Lucy Stone's time. But after the Civil War, she went back to the struggle for women's rights. She continued to speak out—loud and strong. In 1870 she started the *Women's Journal,* a magazine devoted to getting the vote for women. (The magazine lasted for about fifty years, until its cause was won.

After Mrs. Stone's death in 1893, it was edited by her daughter.) Today few people remember the name of Mrs. Henry Brown Blackwell. But many remember Lucy Stone.

15. The passage that came just before this one probably discussed
    (1) slavery
    (2) the first colleges for women
    (3) leaders in the women's rights movement
    (4) magazines before the Civil War
16. The fact that Lucy Stone taught school for a time is
    (1) made clear in the paragraph
    (2) hinted at
    (3) definitely suggested
    (4) not mentioned
17. Of the following, the reader of the passage learns most about
    (1) rural Massachusetts
    (2) public speaking
    (3) women's rights in 1850
    (4) editing magazines
18. The second paragraph makes it clear that women got the vote in about the year
    (1) 1870
    (2) 1888
    (3) 1920
    (4) 1950
19. Henry Brown Blackwell is remembered largely because he
    (1) fought in a war
    (2) was Lucy Stone's husband
    (3) founded Oberlin College
    (4) wrote for the *Women's Journal*
20. In addition to fighting for women's rights, Lucy Stone fought
    (1) against slavery
    (2) big business
    (3) for better schools
    (4) for the handicapped

PUT ALL ANSWERS HERE

1. ① ② ③ ④   11. ① ② ③ ④
2. ① ② ③ ④   12. ① ② ③ ④
3. ① ② ③ ④   13. ① ② ③ ④
4. ① ② ③ ④   14. ① ② ③ ④
5. ① ② ③ ④   15. ① ② ③ ④
6. ① ② ③ ④   16. ① ② ③ ④
7. ① ② ③ ④   17. ① ② ③ ④
8. ① ② ③ ④   18. ① ② ③ ④
9. ① ② ③ ④   19. ① ② ③ ④
10. ① ② ③ ④   20. ① ② ③ ④

READING TEST 5

Directions: Answer the questions on each passage. Fill in the right space between the two lines.

Greenland is the world's largest island. It is in the North Atlantic. Even in the summer, most of it is covered with ice. The population of Eskimos and Europeans is only about 50,000 persons. This is not surprising. What *is* surprising is its name, *Greenland*. The name is deceptive.

The island was discovered about 982 A.D. by Eric the Red, a Viking chief. He probably arrived in the summer. He thought the land along the coast was fit for farming. But who would want to move to the snow-covered land? Eric probably figured that the Icelandic people would be hard to persuade. The name "Greenland" made this job easier.

1. From the selection you can figure out that Eric the Red was NOT
   (A) an explorer
   (B) a chief   A B C D
   (C) a farmer   **1.** ‖ ‖ ‖ ‖
   (D) a sailor
2. The name "Greenland" was
   (A) a good description
   (B) a trick   A B C D
   (C) on all maps in 980 A.D.   **2.** ‖ ‖ ‖ ‖
   (D) the word for "ice" in Icelandic
3. The first people to settle in Greenland probably were
   (A) Norwegian
   (B) English   A B C D
   (C) Dutch   **3.** ‖ ‖ ‖ ‖
   (D) Icelandic
4. The word *deceptive* in paragraph one is
   (A) accurate
   (B) beautiful   A B C D
   (C) incorrectly used   **4.** ‖ ‖ ‖ ‖
   (D) properly spelled with a capital
5. Today, most people in Greenland earn a living
   (A) farming
   (B) fishing   A B C D
   (C) selling ice   **5.** ‖ ‖ ‖ ‖
   (D) (not mentioned)

What's the strangest weather you have ever experienced? Have you ever seen snowdrifts ten feet (3 m) high? Have you ever seen it rain with no clouds overhead? Events like these are not uncommon. But the record for strange weather probably belongs to the "year without a summer."

The famous "year without a summer" was 1816. In states like New York, it snowed every month of the year. It was cool all over the country. Some crops were ruined. In later years, 1816 was called "eighteen hundred and freeze to death."

The year before, a volcano in the Pacific Ocean had erupted. It was one of the biggest blasts on record. Tons of dust went into the air. This dust floated around the world. It may in some way have caused the change in the weather.

6. In the year 1816, the summer was odd because it was
   (A) just like winter
   (B) warm   A B C D
   (C) long   **6.** ‖ ‖ ‖ ‖
   (D) cool
7. Strange events like snow in the middle of July probably occurred
   (A) only in the United States
   (B) only in New York   A B C D
   (C) only in the Pacific   **7.** ‖ ‖ ‖ ‖
   (D) many places in the world
8. Instead of the word *erupted* in paragraph three, the author might have used
   (A) *appeared*
   (B) *failed*   A B C D
   (C) *blown its top*   **8.** ‖ ‖ ‖ ‖
   (D) *measured*
9. The selection gives the reader
   (A) only a cause
   (B) only an effect   A B C D
   (C) effect before cause   **9.** ‖ ‖ ‖ ‖
   (D) cause before effect
10. Which could be removed with the least damage to the purpose of the selection?
   (A) paragraph one
   (B) paragraph two   A B C D
   (C) paragraph three   **10.** ‖ ‖ ‖ ‖
   (D) paragraph one and two